10 minutes a day!

Word Ladders
for Fluency

W0007696

Photocopiable activities to boost reading, vocabulary, spelling and phonics skills

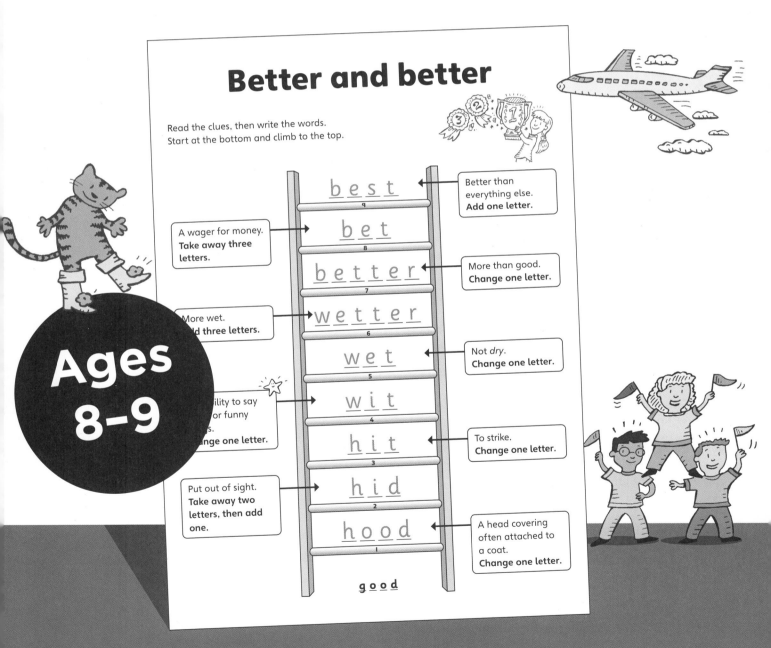

Better and better

Read the clues, then write the words.
Start at the bottom and climb to the top.

b e s t
9

b e t
8

b e t t e r
7

w e t t e r
6

w e t
5

w i t
4

h i t
3

h i d
2

h o o d
1

good

Better than everything else. **Add one letter.**

A wager for money. **Take away three letters.**

More than good. **Change one letter.**

More wet. **Add three letters.**

Not *dry*. **Change one letter.**

...ility to say ... or funny ... **Change one letter.**

To strike. **Change one letter.**

Put out of sight. **Take away two letters, then add one.**

A head covering often attached to a coat. **Change one letter.**

Ages 8-9

Written by Timothy V. Rasinski

Edited by **Herts for Learning**

Published in the UK by Scholastic, 2022

Scholastic Distribution Centre, Bosworth Avenue, Tournament Fields, Warwick, CV34 6UQ

Scholastic Ireland, 89E Lagan Road, Dublin Industrial Estate, Glasnevin, Dublin, DII HP5F

SCHOLASTIC and associated logos are trademarks and/or registered trademarks of Scholastic Inc.

First published in the US by Scholastic Inc, 2005
Text and illustrations © 2005, Timothy Rasinski

© 2022, Scholastic

A CIP catalogue record for this book is available from the British Library.

ISBN 978-0-7023-0936-6

Printed by Bell & Bain Ltd, Glasgow
This product is made of FSC®-certified and other controlled material.

Paper made from wood grown in sustainable forests and other controlled sources.

1 2 3 4 5 6 7 8 9   2 3 4 5 6 7 8 9 0 I

Author
Timothy V. Rasinski

Editorial team
Rachel Morgan, Vicki Yates, Tracey Cowell, Julia Roberts

Design team
Ellen Matlach for Boultinghouse & Boultinghouse, Inc,
Justin Hoffmann, Couper Street Type Co.

Illustration
Teresa Anderko

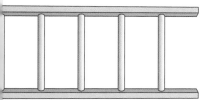

Contents

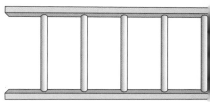

Foreword

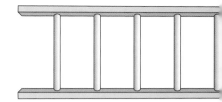

In the UK, the first stage of teaching reading focuses on phonics, with an emphasis on children learning to decode the words on the page. The essential skills of language knowledge, fluency and comprehension are developed alongside.

The National Curriculum states: 'Good comprehension draws from linguistic knowledge (in particular of vocabulary and grammar) and on knowledge of the world.' and that 'Skilled word reading involves both the speedy working out of the pronunciation of unfamiliar printed words (decoding) and the speedy recognition of familiar printed words.'

A breadth of vocabulary is a key component to successful reading comprehension. Much research has shown that the breadth of children's vocabulary has a direct correlation with children's reading comprehension and future life chances. In 2002, Beck, McKeown & Kucan, identified a lack of targeted vocabulary instruction in schools, although, nowadays, most UK schools have a vocabulary development approach woven throughout their curriculum. *Daily Word Ladders for Fluency* will provide schools with an invaluable resource to supplement their approach to developing vocabulary breadth, whilst also reinforcing and embedding decoding skills.

Regular use of these word ladders as part of a rich and varied language development programme can support children to become familiar with a wider range of words and their definitions. They can also reinforce spelling patterns and exceptions that the children are learning. Furthermore, as children read the words from these ladders in context they are supported to read with automaticity (rapid word reading without conscious decoding). This allows

them to read with prosody (expressive, phrased reading) which in turn supports comprehension. Through this fluent reading, the children's knowledge of literary language grows.

Developing a playfulness with words is a further benefit of word ladders. Word problems can encourage an excitement around language and may help train concentration. This, in turn, can encourage further interaction and longer periods of concentration. It is well known that succeeding in solving tricky problems helps to develop confidence and boost self-esteem. Success may then lead to increased acceptance of challenges in other areas of learning. Development of vocabulary also supports an increasing knowledge and understanding of the world. In addition, if children work collaboratively on these ladders, they can be taught to build social and oracy skills and learn to take turns when listening to one another. Aside from practical considerations, vocabulary development can also allow children to appreciate the beauty of our language.

Herts for Learning (HfL) recognises the need to support children who can decode but struggle to understand what they read. The *HfL Reading Fluency Project* was founded on the question: if a child reads a text with expert prosody, can that lead to better understanding? Automatic word recognition is intrinsic to the success of this programme, as automaticity when reading supports an appropriate reading rate which is a crucial element for comprehension. Regular engagement with meaningful language play, such as through word ladder activities, ensures that vocabulary breadth and automatised decoding are developed hand in hand. As such, HfL recognises the word ladders as a useful tool to achieving the aims as outlined in the National Curriculum.

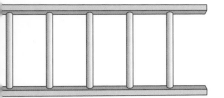
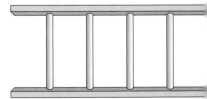

How to use

In this book you'll find 84 mini word study lessons that are also child-pleasing games! To complete each word ladder takes just ten minutes but actively involves each learner in analysing the structure and meaning of words. To play, children begin with one word and then make a series of other words by changing or rearranging the letters in the word before. With regular use, word ladders can go a long way towards developing your children's decoding and vocabulary skills.

How do word ladders work?

Let's say our first word ladder begins with the word *walk*. The instructions will tell children to change one letter in walk to make a word that means 'to speak'. The word children will make is *talk*. The next word will then ask children to make a change in talk to form another word – perhaps *chalk* or *tall*. At the top of the ladder, children will have a final word that is in some way related to the first word – for example, *run*. If children get stuck on a rung along the way, they can come back to it, because the words before and after will give them the clues they need to go on.

How do word ladders benefit children?

Word ladders are great for building children's decoding, phonics, spelling and vocabulary skills. When children add or rearrange letters to make a new word from one they have just made, they must examine sound–symbol relationships closely. This is just the kind of analysis that all children need to perform in order to learn how to decode and spell

accurately. And when the puzzle adds a bit of meaning in the form of a definition (for example, 'Make a word that means to say something'), it helps extend children's understanding of words and concepts. All of these skills are key to children's success in learning to read and write. So even though the word ladders will feel like a game, your children will be practising essential literacy skills at the same time!

How do I teach a word ladder lesson?

Word ladders are incredibly easy and quick to implement. Here are four simple steps:

1. Choose one of the 84 word ladders to try.

2. Make a copy of the word ladder for each child.

3. Choose whether you want to do your word ladders with the class as a whole, or for children to work alone, in pairs, or in groups. (You might do the first few together, until children are ready to work more independently.)

4. For each new word, children will see two clues: the kinds of changes they need to make to the previous word ('Rearrange the letters' or 'Add two letters'), and a definition of or clue to the meaning of the word. Sometimes this clue will be a sentence in which the word is used in context but is left out for children to fill in. Move from word to word this way, up the whole word ladder.

That's the lesson in a nutshell! It should take no longer than ten minutes to do. Once you're finished, you may wish to extend the lesson by asking children to sort

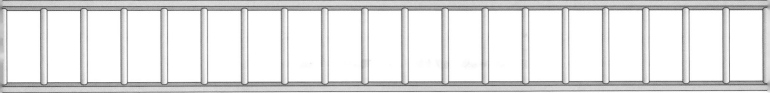

the words into various categories. This can help them deepen their understanding of word relationships. For instance, they could sort them into:

- grammatical categories (Which words are nouns? Verbs?)
- word structure (Which words have a long vowel and which don't? Which contain a consonant blend?)
- word meaning (Which words express what a person can do or feel? Which do not?)

Look for the bonus boxes with stars. These are particularly difficult words you may want to pre-teach. Or you can do these ladders as a group so that children will not get stuck on this rung.

About the author

Timothy V. Rasinski is professor of literacy education at Kent State University in Ohio. He began his career as a classroom teacher. Since then, he's written and edited more than 50 books and 200 articles on reading education, including the best-selling *Megabook of Fluency* and the seminal *The Fluent Reader*.

In 2020, the International Literacy Association awarded Tim the William S. Gray Citation of Merit honour. This award honours a nationally or internationally known individual for their outstanding contributions to the field of reading/ literacy. Of Tim, the International Literacy Association said 'Tim Rasinski is one of those names that's synonymous with high-quality literacy research, resources and professional development, especially when it comes to foundational reading and writing skills and struggling readers.'

Tips for working with word ladders

- List all the 'answers' for the ladder (that is, the words for each rung) in a random order on the whiteboard. Ask children to choose words from the list to complete the puzzle.

- Add your own clues to give children extra help as they work through each rung of a ladder. A recent event in your classroom or community could even inspire clues for words.

- If children are having difficulty with a particular word, you might simply say the word aloud and see if children can spell it correctly by making appropriate changes in the previous word. Elaborate on the meanings of the words as children move their way up the ladder.

- If children are stuck on a particular rung of the word ladder, tell them to skip it and come back to it later.

- Challenge children to come up with alternative definitions for the same words. Many words, like *lock*, *fall* and *stock*, have multiple meanings.

Counting up

Read the clues, then write the words.
Start at the bottom and climb to the top.

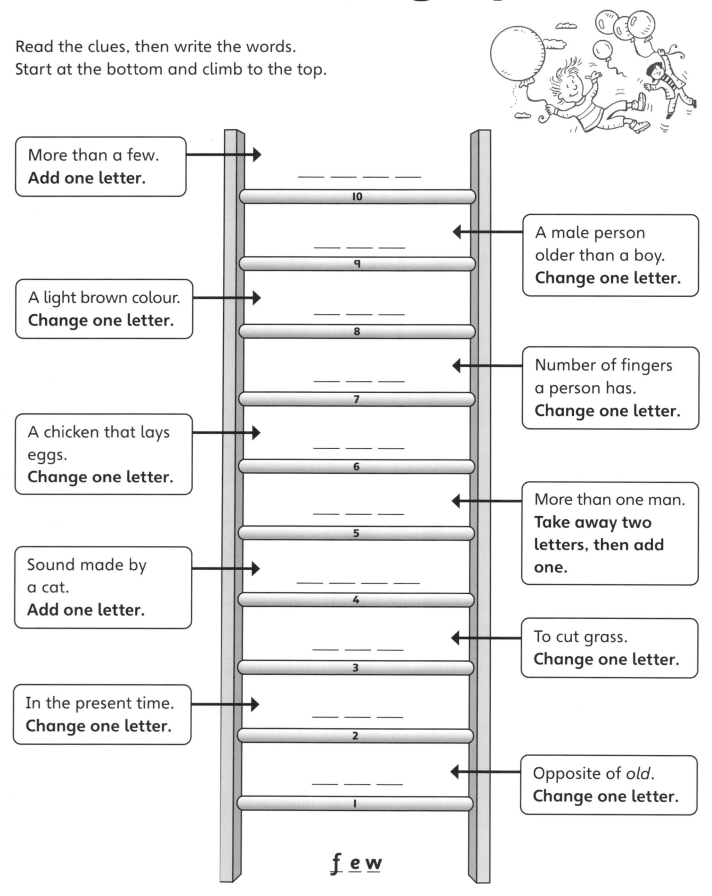

More than a few.
Add one letter.
— — — —
10

A male person older than a boy.
Change one letter.
— — — —
9

A light brown colour.
Change one letter.
— — — —
8

Number of fingers a person has.
Change one letter.
— — — —
7

A chicken that lays eggs.
Change one letter.
— — — —
6

More than one man.
Take away two letters, then add one.
— — —
5

Sound made by a cat.
Add one letter.
— — — —
4

To cut grass.
Change one letter.
— — — —
3

In the present time.
Change one letter.
— — — —
2

Opposite of old.
Change one letter.
— — — —
1

f e w

Name _____

Home, sweet home

Read the clues, then write the words.
Start at the bottom and climb to the top.

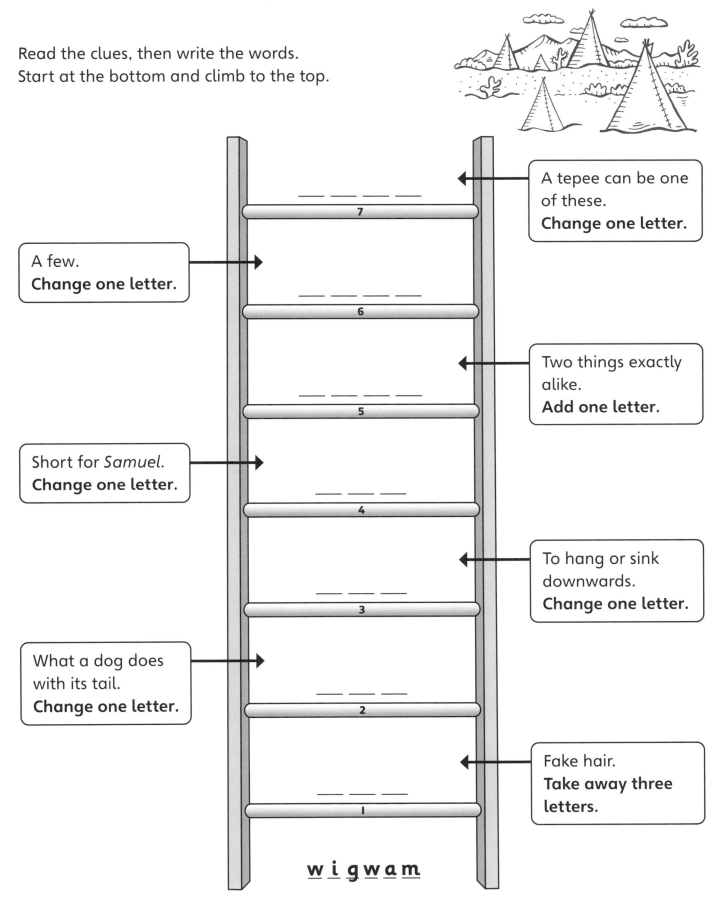

A few.
Change one letter.

A tepee can be one of these.
Change one letter.

Two things exactly alike.
Add one letter.

Short for *Samuel*.
Change one letter.

To hang or sink downwards.
Change one letter.

What a dog does with its tail.
Change one letter.

Fake hair.
Take away three letters.

7
6
5
4
3
2
1

w i g w a m

Name _____

Shrinking sizes

Read the clues, then write the words.
Start at the bottom and climb to the top.

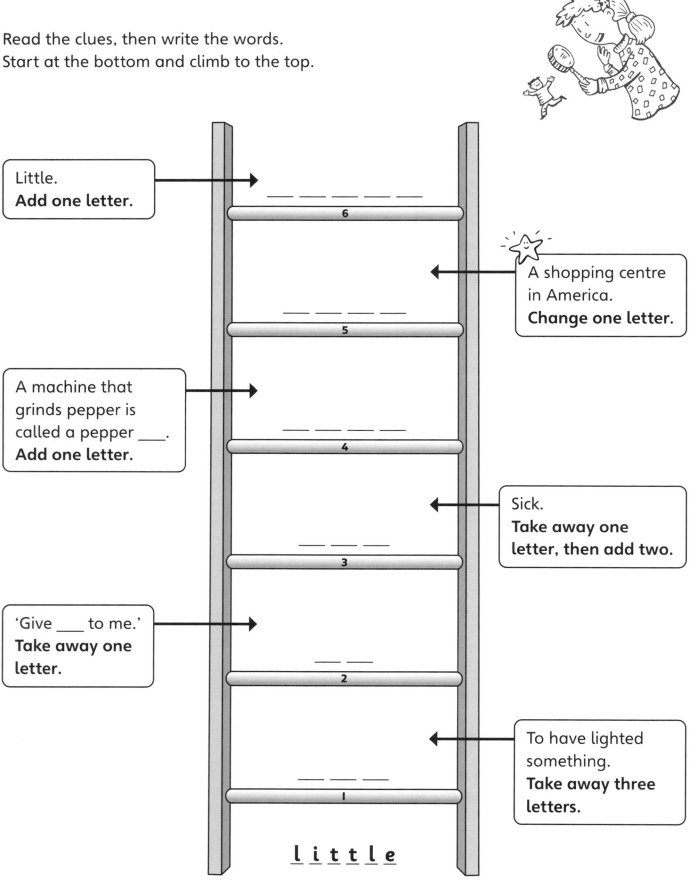

Little.
Add one letter.

A shopping centre in America.
Change one letter.

A machine that grinds pepper is called a pepper ___.
Add one letter.

Sick.
Take away one letter, then add two.

'Give ___ to me.'
Take away one letter.

To have lighted something.
Take away three letters.

6

5

4

3

2

1

l i t t l e

Daily Word Ladders for Fluency ■SCHOLASTIC

Name _____

All wet

Read the clues, then write the words.
Start at the bottom and climb to the top.

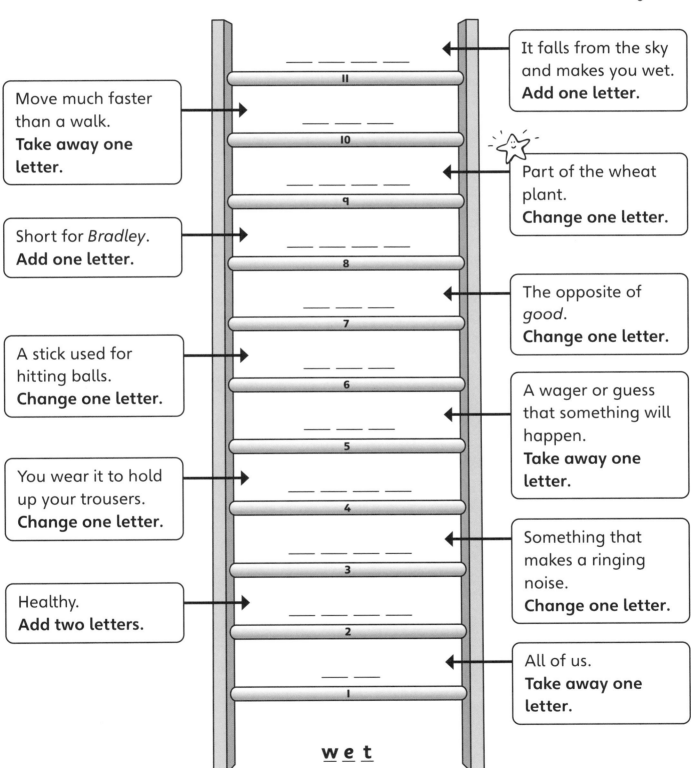

Move much faster than a walk. **Take away one letter.** → (10)

Short for *Bradley*. **Add one letter.** → (8)

A stick used for hitting balls. **Change one letter.** → (6)

You wear it to hold up your trousers. **Change one letter.** → (4)

Healthy. **Add two letters.** → (2)

It falls from the sky and makes you wet. **Add one letter.** ← (11)

Part of the wheat plant. **Change one letter.** ← (9)

The opposite of *good*. **Change one letter.** ← (7)

A wager or guess that something will happen. **Take away one letter.** ← (5)

Something that makes a ringing noise. **Change one letter.** ← (3)

All of us. **Take away one letter.** ← (1)

w e t

Name _____

Go, go, go

Read the clues, then write the words.
Start at the bottom and climb to the top.

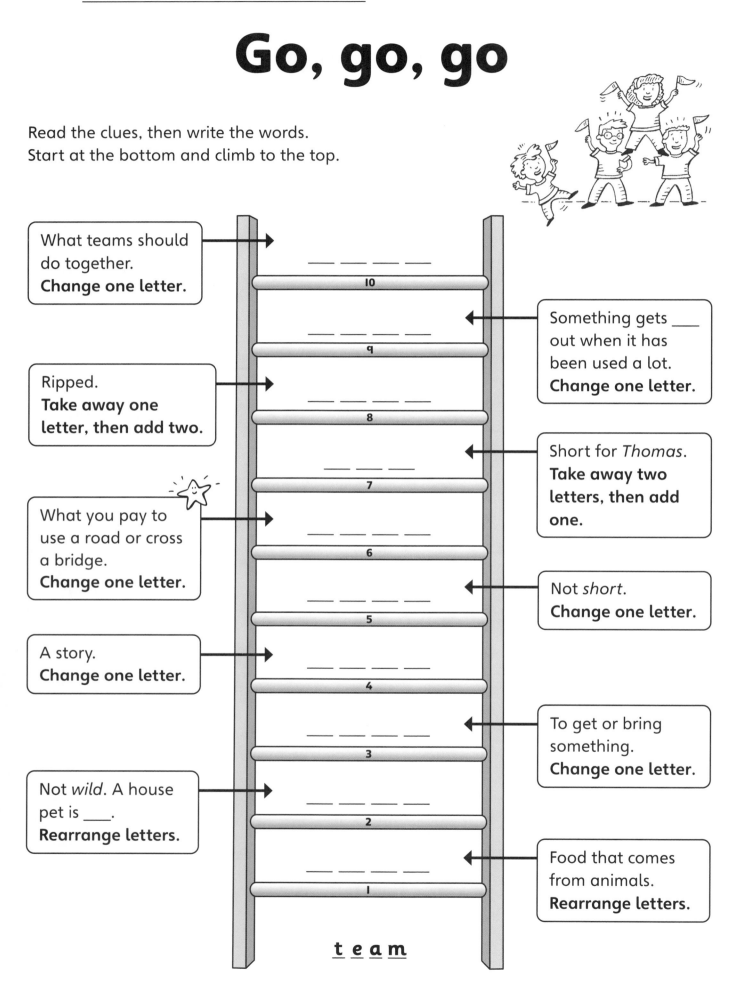

What teams should do together.
Change one letter.

Something gets ___ out when it has been used a lot.
Change one letter.

Ripped.
Take away one letter, then add two.

Short for *Thomas*.
Take away two letters, then add one.

What you pay to use a road or cross a bridge.
Change one letter.

Not *short*.
Change one letter.

A story.
Change one letter.

To get or bring something.
Change one letter.

Not *wild*. A house pet is ___.
Rearrange letters.

Food that comes from animals.
Rearrange letters.

10
9
8
7
6
5
4
3
2
1

t e a m

Daily Word Ladders for Fluency **SCHOLASTIC**

Name _____

Sweet seasons

Read the clues, then write the words.
Start at the bottom and climb to the top.

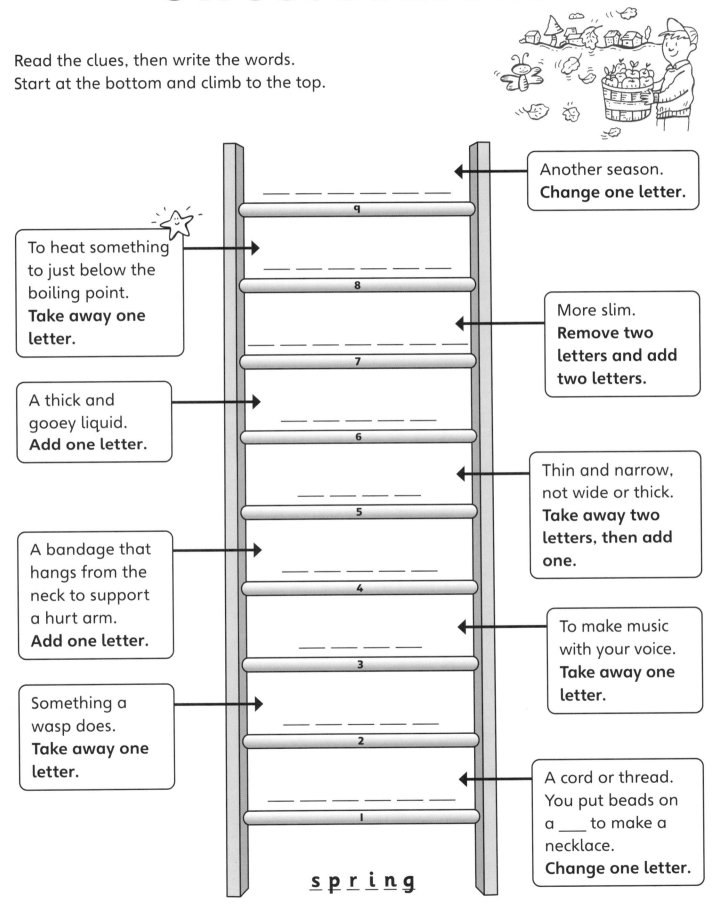

Another season.
Change one letter.

To heat something to just below the boiling point.
Take away one letter.

More slim.
Remove two letters and add two letters.

A thick and gooey liquid.
Add one letter.

Thin and narrow, not wide or thick.
Take away two letters, then add one.

A bandage that hangs from the neck to support a hurt arm.
Add one letter.

To make music with your voice.
Take away one letter.

Something a wasp does.
Take away one letter.

A cord or thread. You put beads on a ___ to make a necklace.
Change one letter.

9

8

7

6

5

4

3

2

1

s p r i n g

Art smart

Read the clues, then write the words.
Start at the bottom and climb to the top.

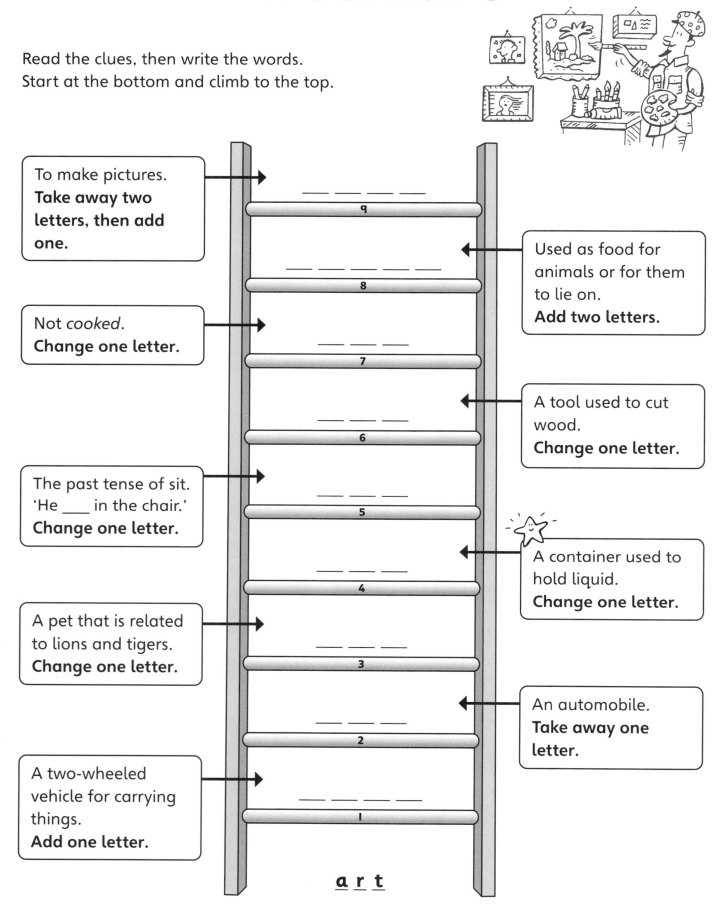

To make pictures.
Take away two letters, then add one.

9 _ _ _ _ _

Used as food for animals or for them to lie on.
Add two letters.

8 _ _ _ _ _

Not *cooked*.
Change one letter.

7 _ _ _ _

A tool used to cut wood.
Change one letter.

6 _ _ _ _

The past tense of sit.
'He ___ in the chair.'
Change one letter.

5 _ _ _

A container used to hold liquid.
Change one letter.

4 _ _ _

A pet that is related to lions and tigers.
Change one letter.

3 _ _ _

An automobile.
Take away one letter.

2 _ _ _

A two-wheeled vehicle for carrying things.
Add one letter.

1 _ _ _ _

<u>a</u> <u>r</u> <u>t</u>

Name _____

Bedtime

Read the clues, then write the words.
Start at the bottom and climb to the top.

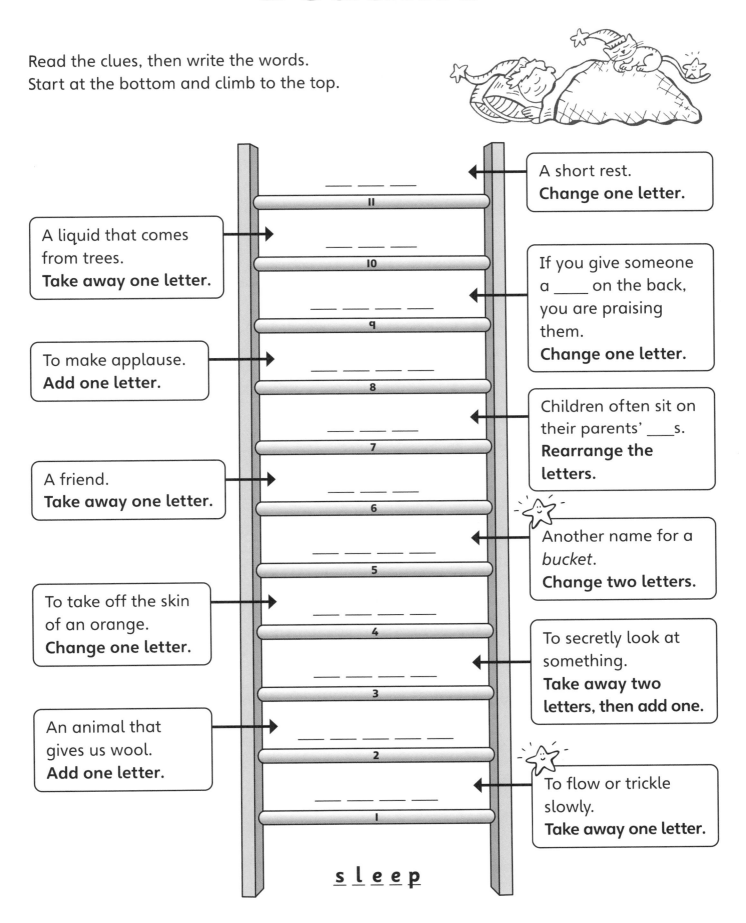

A liquid that comes from trees.
Take away one letter.

To make applause.
Add one letter.

A friend.
Take away one letter.

To take off the skin of an orange.
Change one letter.

An animal that gives us wool.
Add one letter.

A short rest.
Change one letter.

If you give someone a _____ on the back, you are praising them.
Change one letter.

Children often sit on their parents' ___s.
Rearrange the letters.

Another name for a *bucket*.
Change two letters.

To secretly look at something.
Take away two letters, then add one.

To flow or trickle slowly.
Take away one letter.

11
10
9
8
7
6
5
4
3
2
1

s l e e p

Name _____

More or less

Read the clues, then write the words.
Start at the bottom and climb to the top.

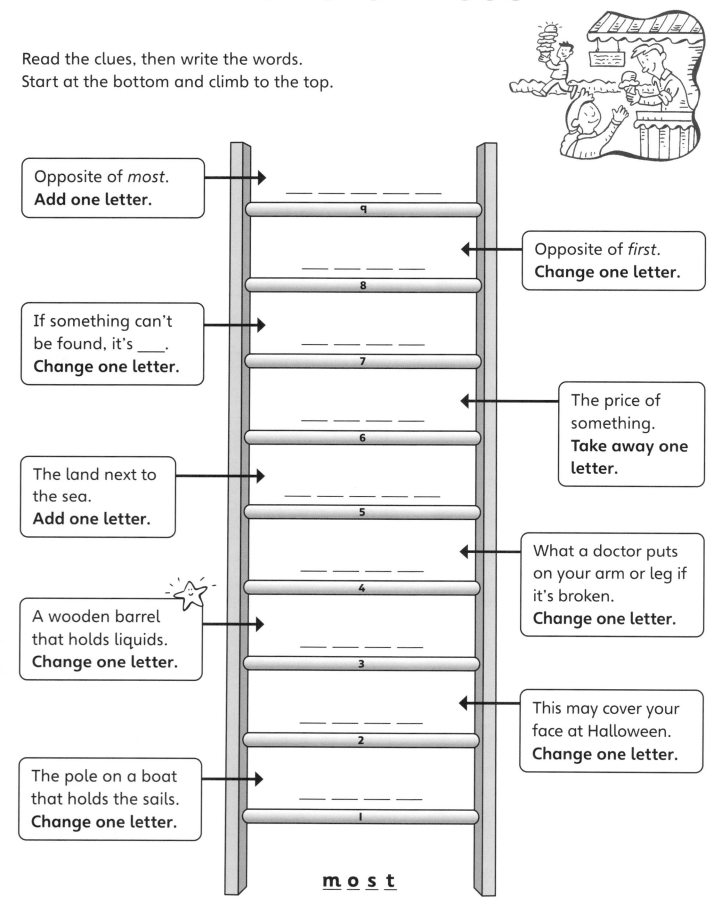

Opposite of *most*.
Add one letter.
→ 9 _ _ _ _ _

8 _ _ _ _ _
← Opposite of *first*.
Change one letter.

If something can't
be found, it's ___.
Change one letter.
→ 7 _ _ _ _

6 _ _ _ _
← The price of
something.
**Take away one
letter.**

The land next to
the sea.
Add one letter.
→ 5 _ _ _ _ _

4 _ _ _ _
← What a doctor puts
on your arm or leg if
it's broken.
Change one letter.

A wooden barrel
that holds liquids.
Change one letter.
→ 3 _ _ _ _

2 _ _ _ _
← This may cover your
face at Halloween.
Change one letter.

The pole on a boat
that holds the sails.
Change one letter.
→ 1 _ _ _ _

<u>m</u> <u>o</u> <u>s</u> <u>t</u>

Photocopiable

Daily Word Ladders for Fluency **SCHOLASTIC**

Hair care

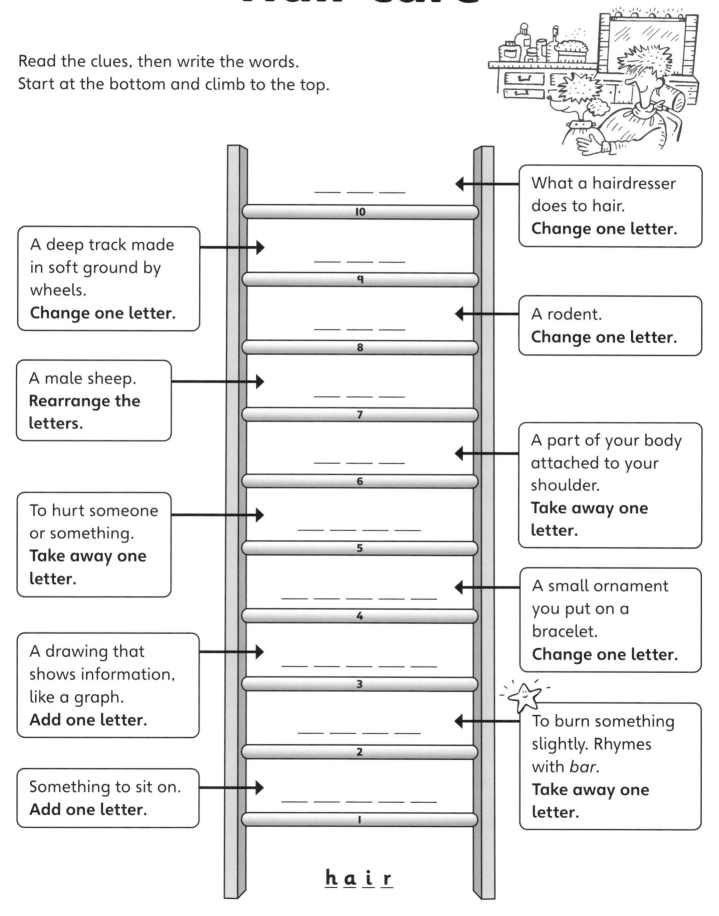

Read the clues, then write the words.
Start at the bottom and climb to the top.

What a hairdresser does to hair. **Change one letter.**

A deep track made in soft ground by wheels. **Change one letter.**

A rodent. **Change one letter.**

A male sheep. **Rearrange the letters.**

A part of your body attached to your shoulder. **Take away one letter.**

To hurt someone or something. **Take away one letter.**

A small ornament you put on a bracelet. **Change one letter.**

A drawing that shows information, like a graph. **Add one letter.**

To burn something slightly. Rhymes with *bar*. **Take away one letter.**

Something to sit on. **Add one letter.**

h a i r

Name _____

Inside out

Read the clues, then write the words.
Start at the bottom and climb to the top.

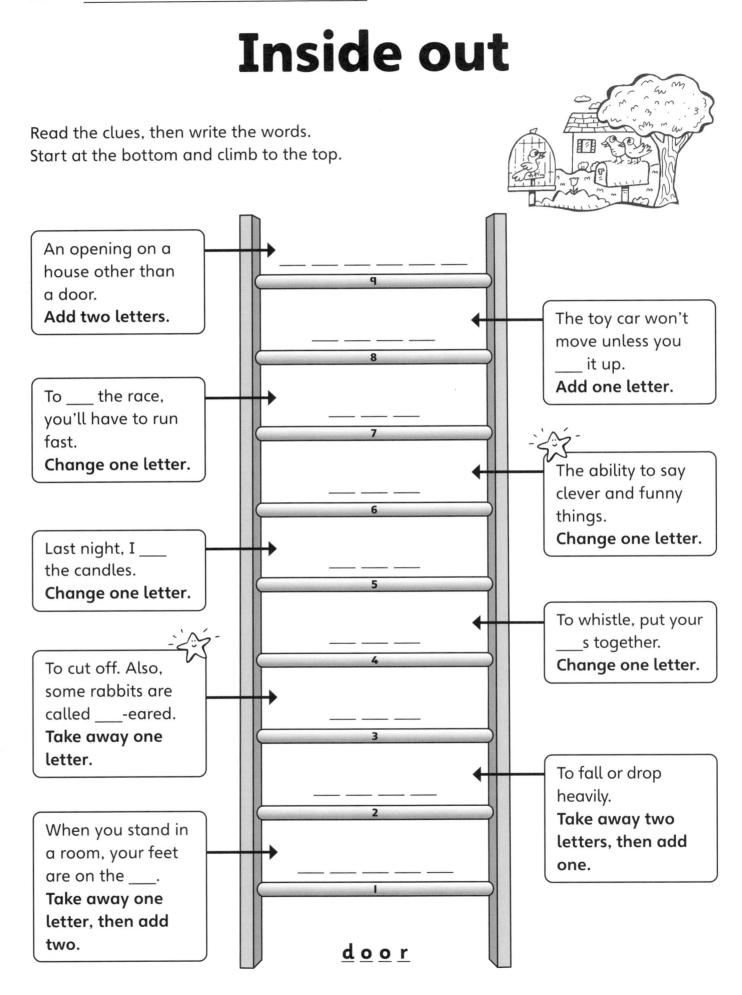

An opening on a house other than a door.
Add two letters.

→ 9 _ _ _ _ _ _

The toy car won't move unless you ___ it up.
Add one letter.
← 8 _ _ _ _ _

To ___ the race, you'll have to run fast.
Change one letter.

→ 7 _ _ _ _

The ability to say clever and funny things.
Change one letter.
← 6 _ _ _

Last night, I ___ the candles.
Change one letter.

→ 5 _ _ _ _

To whistle, put your ___s together.
Change one letter.
← 4 _ _ _

To cut off. Also, some rabbits are called ___-eared.
Take away one letter.

→ 3 _ _ _

To fall or drop heavily.
Take away two letters, then add one.
← 2 _ _ _ _

When you stand in a room, your feet are on the ___.
Take away one letter, then add two.

→ 1 _ _ _ _ _

d o o r

Daily Word Ladders for Fluency **SCHOLASTIC**

Dogs

Read the clues, then write the words.
Start at the bottom and climb to the top.

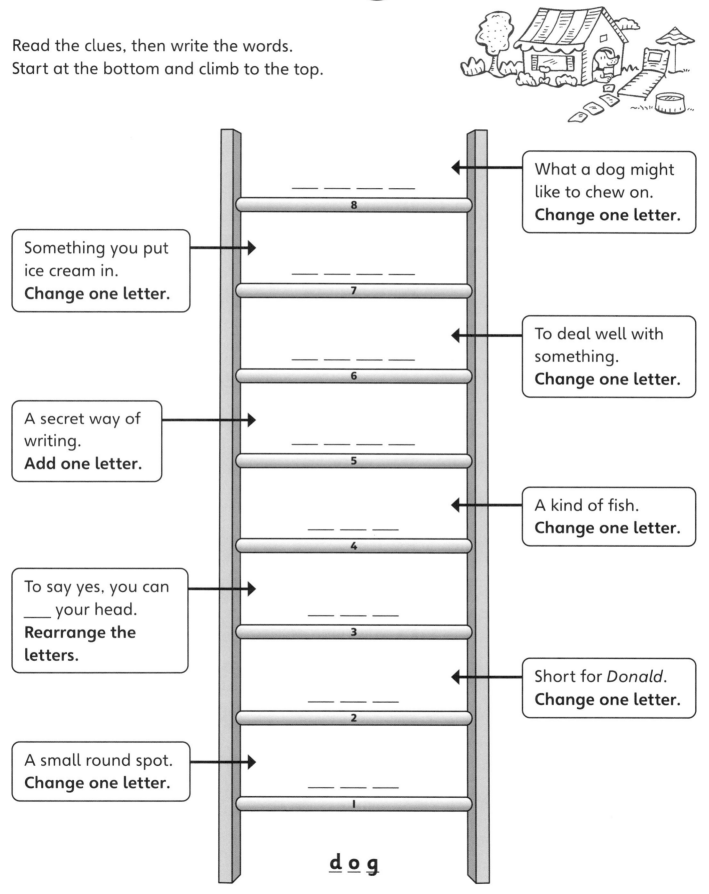

What a dog might like to chew on.
Change one letter.

Something you put ice cream in.
Change one letter.

To deal well with something.
Change one letter.

A secret way of writing.
Add one letter.

A kind of fish.
Change one letter.

To say yes, you can ___ your head.
Rearrange the letters.

Short for *Donald*.
Change one letter.

A small round spot.
Change one letter.

8

7

6

5

4

3

2

1

d o g

Name _____

Restful holiday

Read the clues, then write the words.
Start at the bottom and climb to the top.

What you do at night.
Change two letters.

9 _ _ _ _ _

Covering for a mattress.
Change two letters.

8 _ _ _ _ _

To take pictures with a camera.
Add one letter.

7 _ _ _ _ _ _

A kick that you hope will score a goal in football. 'What a great ___!'
Rearrange the letters.

6 _ _ _ _ _

A person who throws a party.
Take away one letter and change one letter.

5 _ _ _ _ _

Speed or quickness in doing something.
Add one letter.

4 _ _ _ _ _ _

The opposite of *love*.
Add one letter.

3 _ _ _ _ _

Covers your head.
Change one letter.

2 _ _ _ _

Very warm.
Take away two letters.

1 _ _ _ _

h o t e l

Gardening

Read the clues, then write the words.
Start at the bottom and climb to the top.

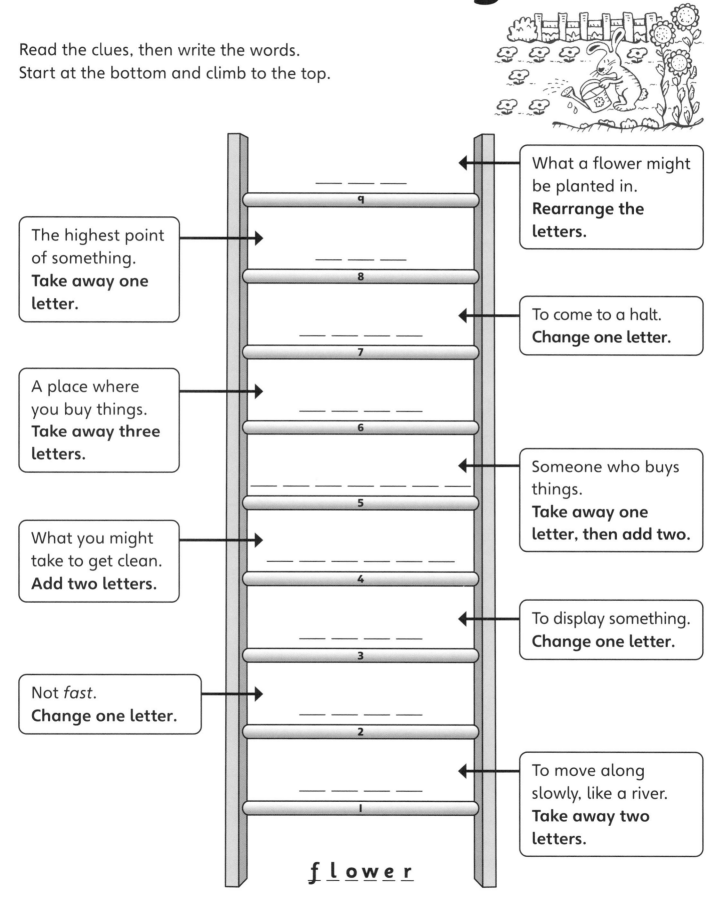

What a flower might be planted in. **Rearrange the letters.**

The highest point of something. **Take away one letter.**

To come to a halt. **Change one letter.**

A place where you buy things. **Take away three letters.**

Someone who buys things. **Take away one letter, then add two.**

What you might take to get clean. **Add two letters.**

To display something. **Change one letter.**

Not *fast*. **Change one letter.**

To move along slowly, like a river. **Take away two letters.**

9

8

7

6

5

4

3

2

1

f l o w e r

Name _____

Shady glade

Read the clues, then write the words.
Start at the bottom and climb to the top.

What gives you shade outdoors. Add one letter. → _ _ _ _ _ 10

_ _ _ _ 9 ← **Golfers put a golf ball on this. Change one letter.**

To view. Take away one letter. → _ _ _ _ 8

_ _ _ _ _ 7 ← **To flow or trickle slowly. Take away one letter, then add two.**

To drink just a little. Change one letter. → _ _ _ _ 6

_ _ _ _ 5 ← **A liquid that comes from trees. Change one letter.**

Short for Samuel. Take away one letter. → _ _ _ 4

_ _ _ _ _ 3 ← **Exactly alike. Take away one letter.**

A bad feeling after doing something wrong. Change one letter. → _ _ _ _ _ _ 2

_ _ _ _ _ _ 1 ← **Triangles and squares are ___s. Change one letter.**

<u>s h a d e</u>

Daily Word Ladders for Fluency ■SCHOLASTIC

Name _____

Transportation

Read the clues, then write the words.
Start at the bottom and climb to the top.

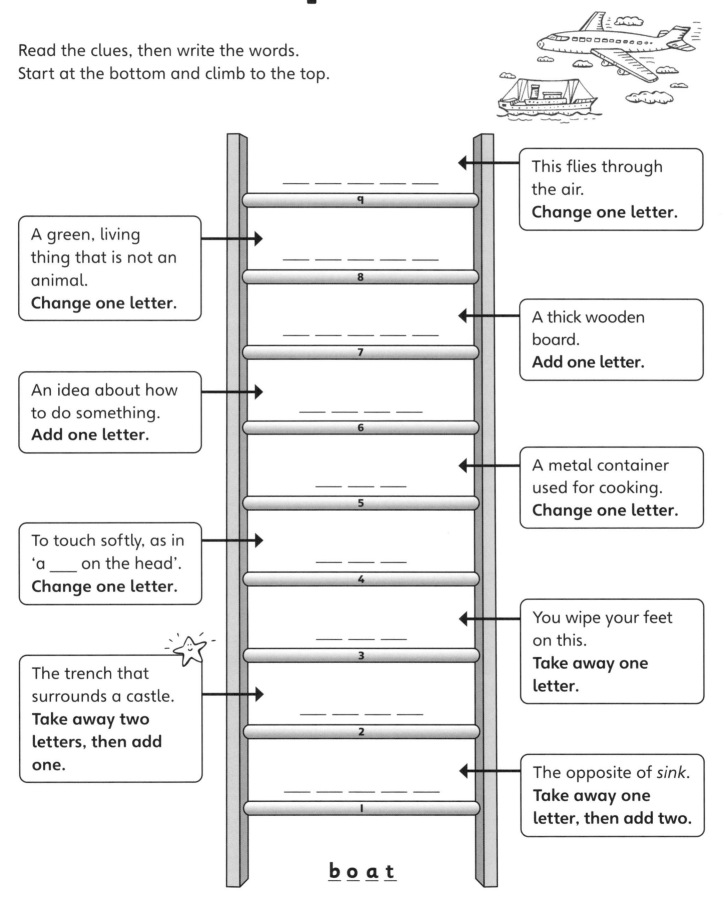

This flies through the air.
Change one letter.

A green, living thing that is not an animal.
Change one letter.

A thick wooden board.
Add one letter.

An idea about how to do something.
Add one letter.

A metal container used for cooking.
Change one letter.

To touch softly, as in 'a ___ on the head'.
Change one letter.

You wipe your feet on this.
Take away one letter.

The trench that surrounds a castle.
Take away two letters, then add one.

The opposite of *sink*.
Take away one letter, then add two.

9

8

7

6

5

4

3

2

1

b o a t

Good cooking

Read the clues, then write the words.
Start at the bottom and climb to the top.

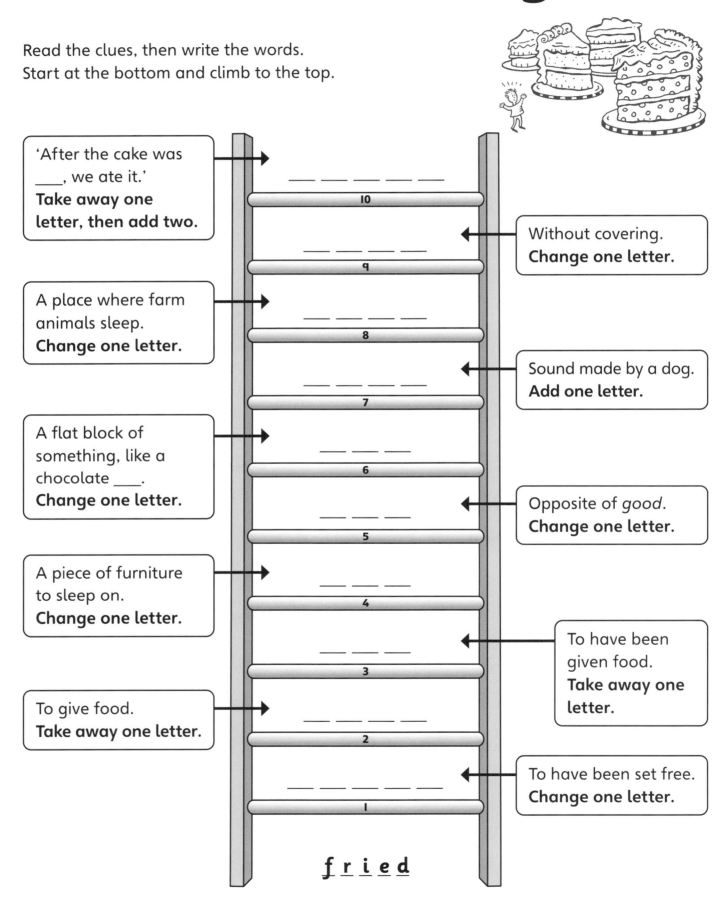

'After the cake was ___, we ate it.'
Take away one letter, then add two.

10 _ _ _ _ _

Without covering.
Change one letter.

9 _ _ _ _

A place where farm animals sleep.
Change one letter.

8 _ _ _ _

Sound made by a dog.
Add one letter.

7 _ _ _ _ _

A flat block of something, like a chocolate ___.
Change one letter.

6 _ _ _ _

Opposite of *good*.
Change one letter.

5 _ _ _ _

A piece of furniture to sleep on.
Change one letter.

4 _ _ _ _

To have been given food.
Take away one letter.

3 _ _ _ _

To give food.
Take away one letter.

2 _ _ _ _ _

To have been set free.
Change one letter.

1 _ _ _ _ _

f r i e d

Finish line

Read the clues, then write the words.
Start at the bottom and climb to the top.

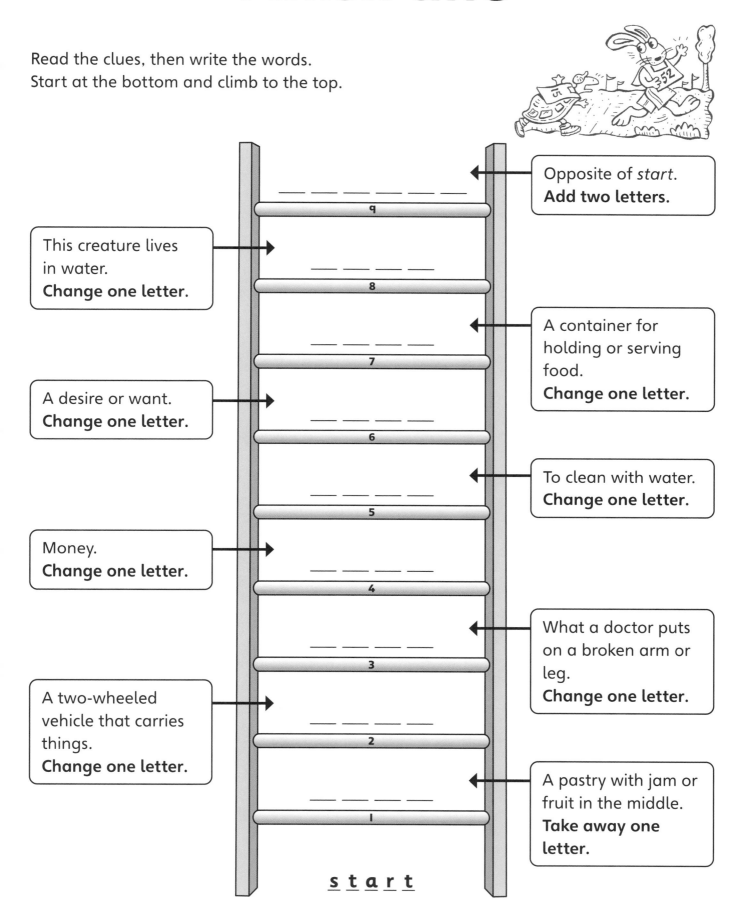

9 _ _ _ _ _ _ _ — Opposite of *start*. **Add two letters.**

This creature lives in water. **Change one letter.** → **8** _ _ _ _ _

7 _ _ _ _ _ — A container for holding or serving food. **Change one letter.**

A desire or want. **Change one letter.** → **6** _ _ _ _

5 _ _ _ _ — To clean with water. **Change one letter.**

Money. **Change one letter.** → **4** _ _ _ _

3 _ _ _ _ _ — What a doctor puts on a broken arm or leg. **Change one letter.**

A two-wheeled vehicle that carries things. **Change one letter.** → **2** _ _ _ _ _

1 _ _ _ _ _ — A pastry with jam or fruit in the middle. **Take away one letter.**

s t a r t

Name _____

Fireworks

Read the clues, then write the words.
Start at the bottom and climb to the top.

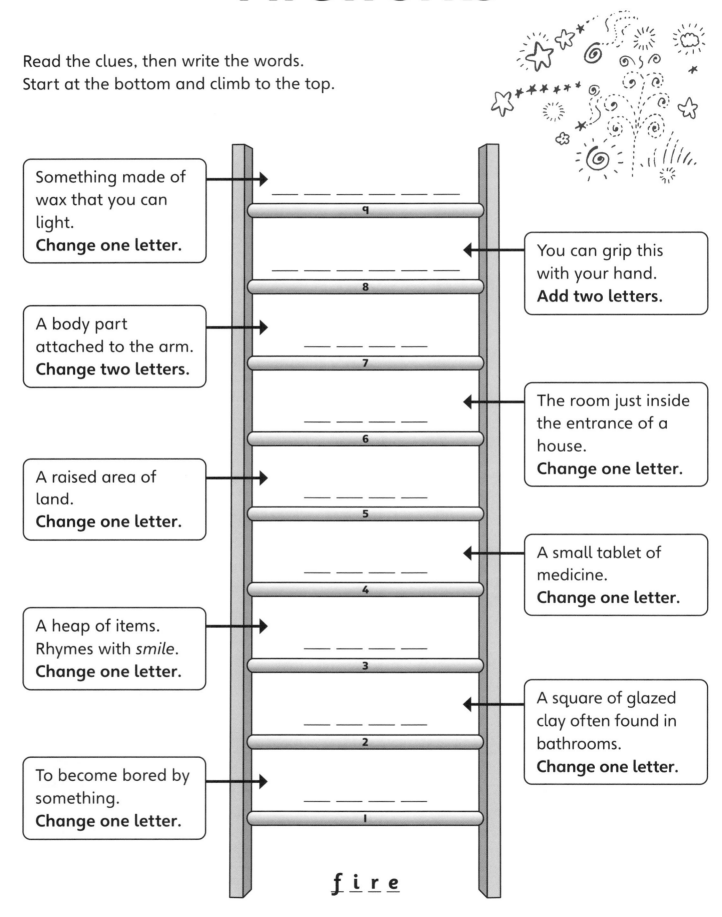

Something made of wax that you can light.
Change one letter.

→ _ _ _ _ _ _ 9

_ _ _ _ _ 8 ← You can grip this with your hand. **Add two letters.**

A body part attached to the arm.
Change two letters.

→ _ _ _ _ 7

_ _ _ _ 6 ← The room just inside the entrance of a house. **Change one letter.**

A raised area of land.
Change one letter.

→ _ _ _ _ 5

_ _ _ _ 4 ← A small tablet of medicine. **Change one letter.**

A heap of items. Rhymes with *smile*.
Change one letter.

→ _ _ _ _ 3

_ _ _ _ 2 ← A square of glazed clay often found in bathrooms. **Change one letter.**

To become bored by something.
Change one letter.

→ _ _ _ _ 1

f i r e

Daily Word Ladders for Fluency **SCHOLASTIC**

Name _____

Opposites attract 1

Read the clues, then write the words.
Start at the bottom and climb to the top.

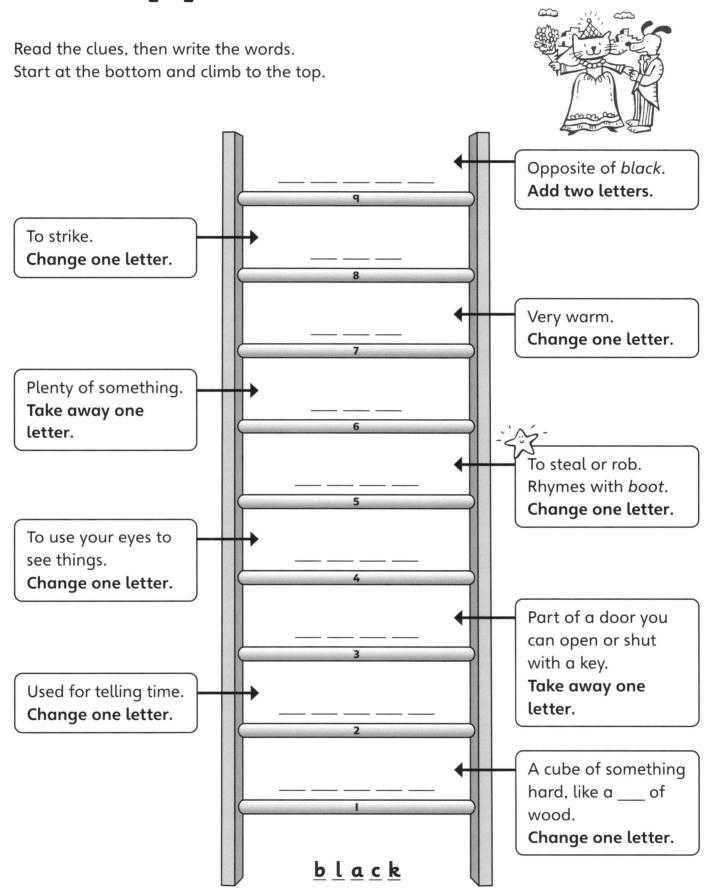

9. _ _ _ _ _

Opposite of *black*.
Add two letters.

To strike.
Change one letter.

8. _ _ _ _

Very warm.
Change one letter.

7. _ _ _ _

Plenty of something.
Take away one letter.

6. _ _ _ _

To steal or rob.
Rhymes with *boot*.
Change one letter.

5. _ _ _ _ _

To use your eyes to see things.
Change one letter.

4. _ _ _ _

Part of a door you can open or shut with a key.
Take away one letter.

3. _ _ _ _ _

Used for telling time.
Change one letter.

2. _ _ _ _ _

A cube of something hard, like a ___ of wood.
Change one letter.

1. _ _ _ _ _

b l a c k

Name _____

Seasoning selection

Read the clues, then write the words.
Start at the bottom and climb to the top.

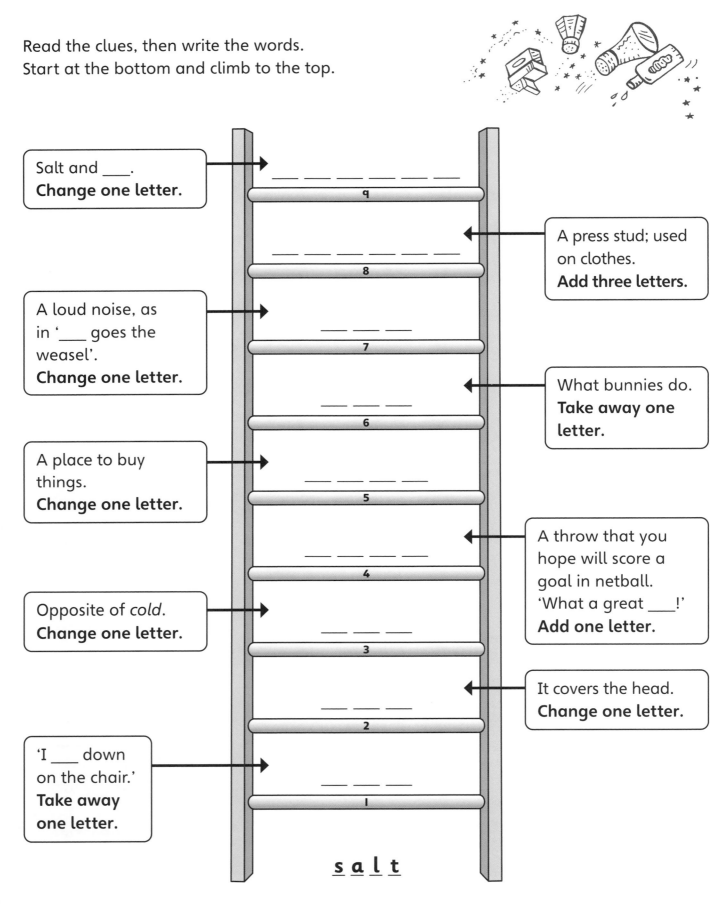

Salt and ___.
Change one letter.
→ _ _ _ _ _ 9

_ _ _ _ _ _ 8
← A press stud; used on clothes. **Add three letters.**

A loud noise, as in '___ goes the weasel'.
Change one letter.
→ _ _ _ _ 7

_ _ _ _ 6
← What bunnies do. **Take away one letter.**

A place to buy things.
Change one letter.
→ _ _ _ _ _ 5

_ _ _ _ _ 4
← A throw that you hope will score a goal in netball. 'What a great ___!' **Add one letter.**

Opposite of *cold*.
Change one letter.
→ _ _ _ _ 3

_ _ _ _ 2
← It covers the head. **Change one letter.**

'I ___ down on the chair.'
Take away one letter.
→ _ _ _ _ 1

<u>s</u> <u>a</u> <u>l</u> <u>t</u>

Daily Word Ladders for Fluency **SCHOLASTIC**

Name _____

Displays of affection

Read the clues, then write the words.
Start at the bottom and climb to the top.

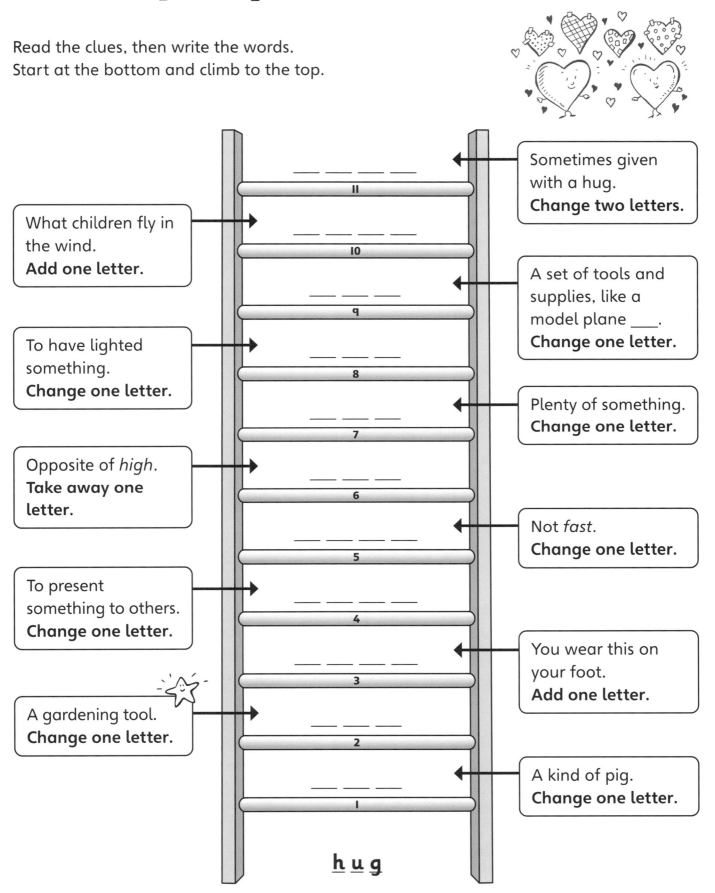

Sometimes given with a hug. Change two letters. → (11)

What children fly in the wind. Add one letter. → (10)

A set of tools and supplies, like a model plane ___. Change one letter. → (9)

To have lighted something. Change one letter. → (8)

Plenty of something. Change one letter. → (7)

Opposite of *high*. Take away one letter. → (6)

Not *fast*. Change one letter. → (5)

To present something to others. Change one letter. → (4)

You wear this on your foot. Add one letter. → (3)

A gardening tool. Change one letter. → (2)

A kind of pig. Change one letter. → (1)

h u g

Neigh-bours

Read the clues, then write the words.
Start at the bottom and climb to the top.

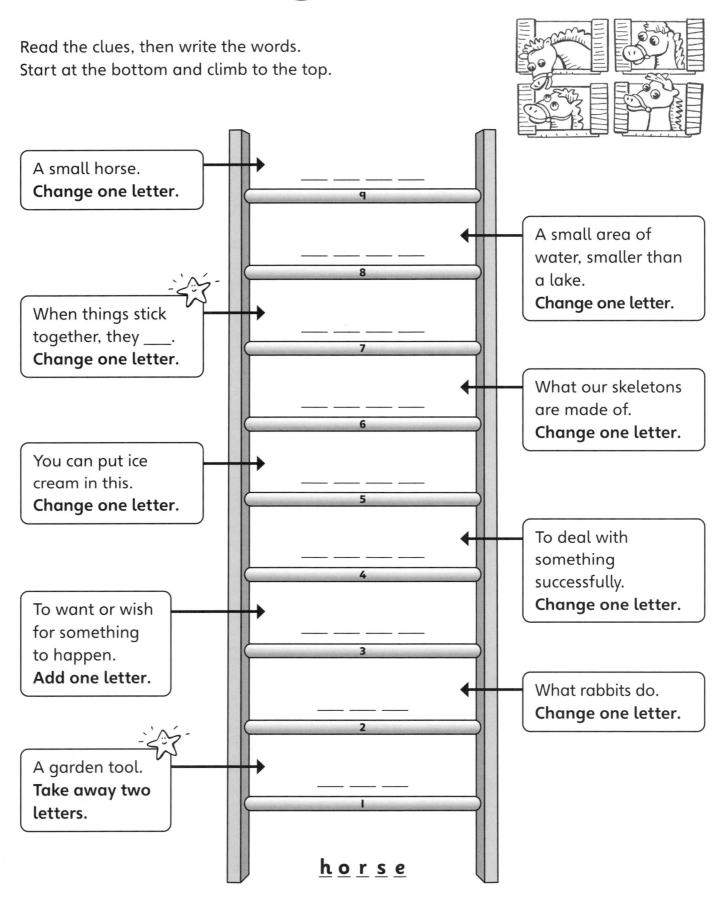

A small horse.
Change one letter.

9 _ _ _ _ _

A small area of
water, smaller than
a lake.
Change one letter.

8 _ _ _ _ _

When things stick
together, they ___.
Change one letter.

7 _ _ _ _ _

What our skeletons
are made of.
Change one letter.

6 _ _ _ _ _

You can put ice
cream in this.
Change one letter.

5 _ _ _ _ _

To deal with
something
successfully.
Change one letter.

4 _ _ _ _ _

To want or wish
for something
to happen.
Add one letter.

3 _ _ _ _ _

What rabbits do.
Change one letter.

2 _ _ _ _

A garden tool.
**Take away two
letters.**

1 _ _ _ _

h o r s e

Daily Word Ladders for Fluency **SCHOLASTIC**

Name _____

Giving and receiving

Read the clues, then write the words.
Start at the bottom and climb to the top.

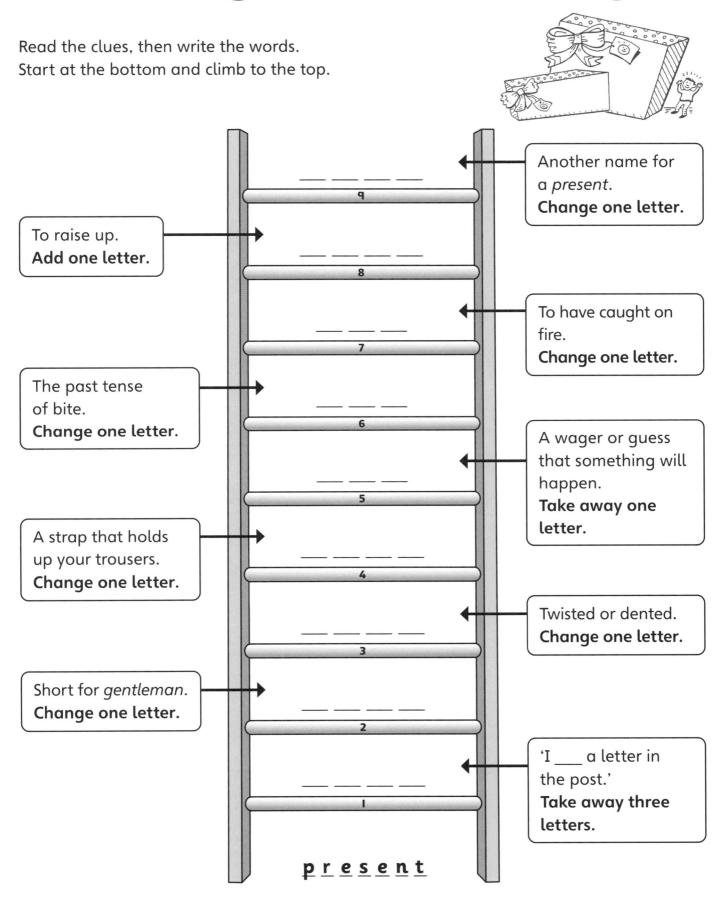

Another name for a *present*.
Change one letter.

To raise up.
Add one letter.

To have caught on fire.
Change one letter.

The past tense of bite.
Change one letter.

A wager or guess that something will happen.
Take away one letter.

A strap that holds up your trousers.
Change one letter.

Twisted or dented.
Change one letter.

Short for *gentleman*.
Change one letter.

'I ___ a letter in the post.'
Take away three letters.

9

8

7

6

5

4

3

2

1

p r e s e n t

Getting there

Read the clues, then write the words.
Start at the bottom and climb to the top.

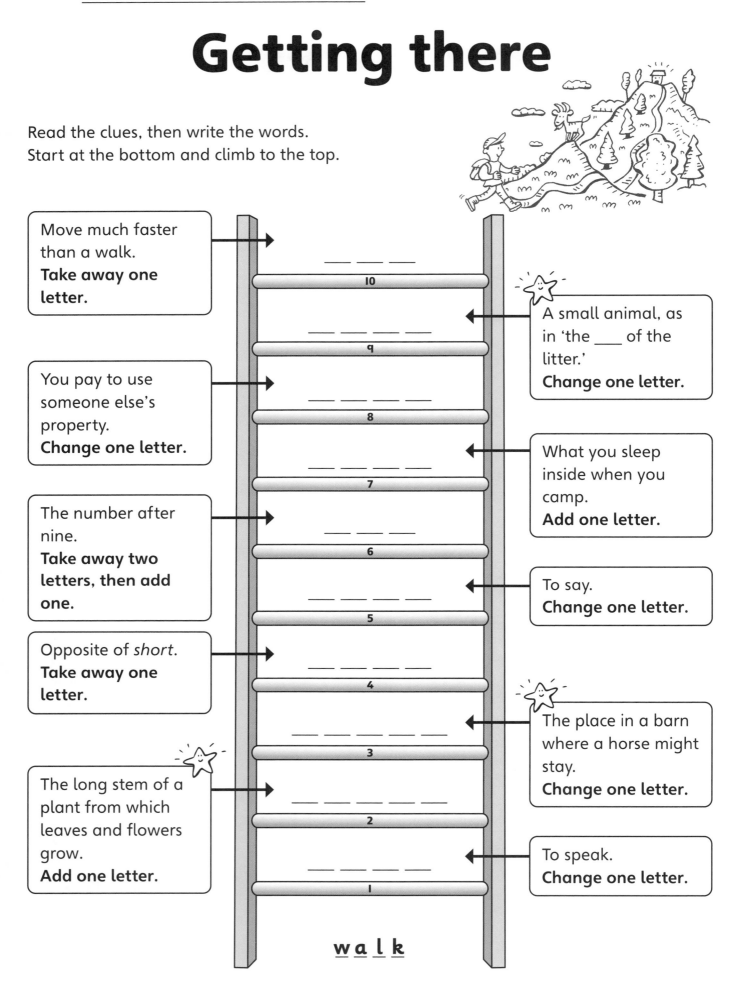

Move much faster than a walk. **Take away one letter.**

— — — — (10)

A small animal, as in 'the ___ of the litter.' **Change one letter.**

— — — — — (9)

You pay to use someone else's property. **Change one letter.**

— — — — (8)

What you sleep inside when you camp. **Add one letter.**

— — — — — (7)

The number after nine. **Take away two letters, then add one.**

— — — — (6)

To say. **Change one letter.**

— — — — — (5)

Opposite of *short*. **Take away one letter.**

— — — — — (4)

The place in a barn where a horse might stay. **Change one letter.**

— — — — — — (3)

The long stem of a plant from which leaves and flowers grow. **Add one letter.**

— — — — — (2)

To speak. **Change one letter.**

— — — — (1)

w a l k

Daily Word Ladders for Fluency **SCHOLASTIC**

Name _____

Splish splash

Read the clues, then write the words.
Start at the bottom and climb to the top.

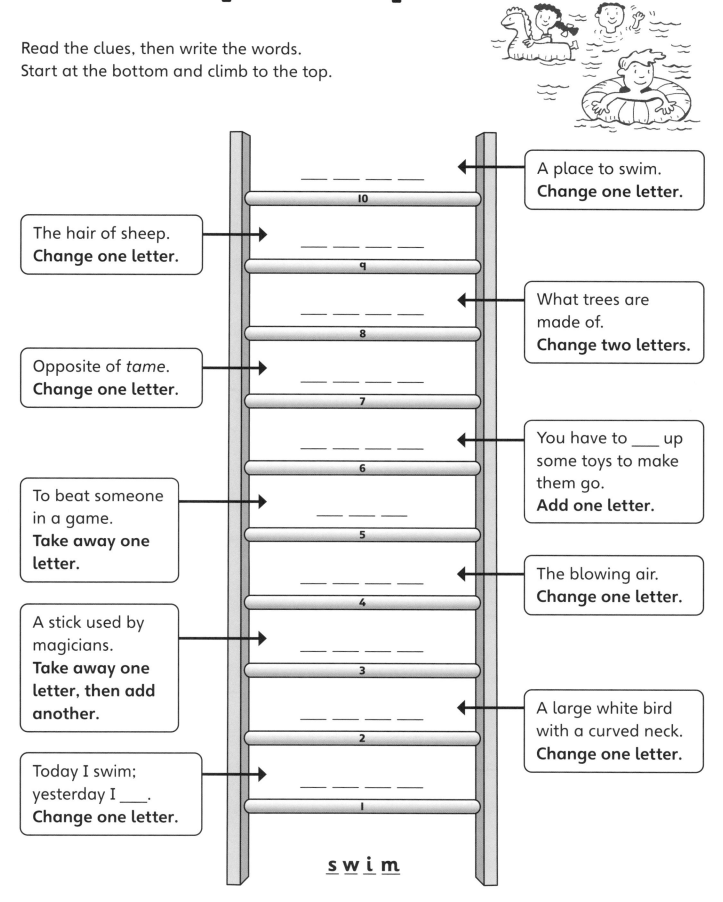

A place to swim.
Change one letter.

The hair of sheep.
Change one letter.

10

What trees are made of.
Change two letters.

9

8

Opposite of *tame*.
Change one letter.

7

You have to ___ up some toys to make them go.
Add one letter.

6

To beat someone in a game.
Take away one letter.

5

The blowing air.
Change one letter.

4

A stick used by magicians.
Take away one letter, then add another.

3

A large white bird with a curved neck.
Change one letter.

2

Today I swim; yesterday I ___.
Change one letter.

1

s w i m

Fancy footwear

Read the clues, then write the words.
Start at the bottom and climb to the top.

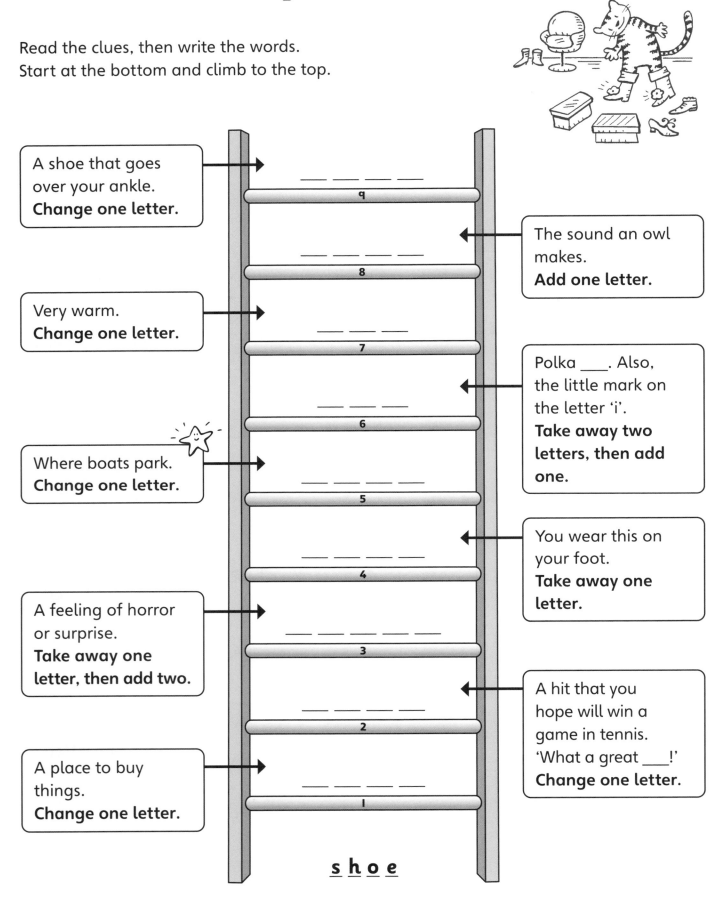

A shoe that goes over your ankle. **Change one letter.**

The sound an owl makes. **Add one letter.**

Very warm. **Change one letter.**

Polka ___. Also, the little mark on the letter 'i'. **Take away two letters, then add one.**

Where boats park. **Change one letter.**

You wear this on your foot. **Take away one letter.**

A feeling of horror or surprise. **Take away one letter, then add two.**

A hit that you hope will win a game in tennis. 'What a great ___!' **Change one letter.**

A place to buy things. **Change one letter.**

9

8

7

6

5

4

3

2

1

s h o e

Daily Word Ladders for Fluency **SCHOLASTIC**

Name _____

Woodcutter

Read the clues, then write the words.
Start at the bottom and climb to the top.

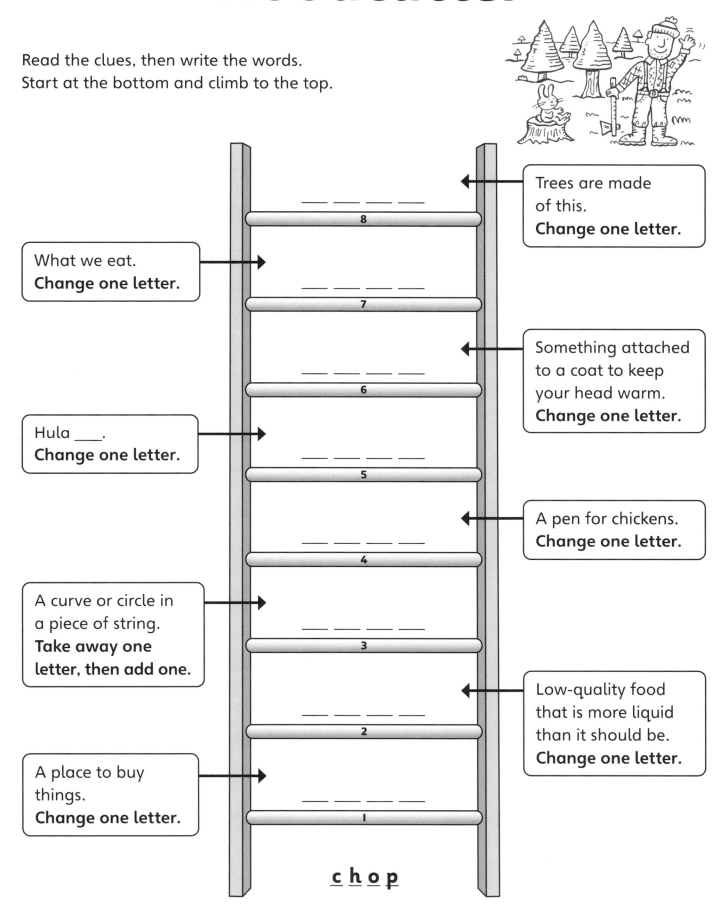

Trees are made of this.
Change one letter.
— — — — (8)

What we eat.
Change one letter.
— — — — (7)

Something attached to a coat to keep your head warm.
Change one letter.
— — — — (6)

Hula ___.
Change one letter.
— — — — (5)

A pen for chickens.
Change one letter.
— — — — (4)

A curve or circle in a piece of string.
Take away one letter, then add one.
— — — — (3)

Low-quality food that is more liquid than it should be.
Change one letter.
— — — — (2)

A place to buy things.
Change one letter.
— — — — (1)

c h o p

Name _____

Wonderful whales

Read the clues, then write the words.
Start at the bottom and climb to the top.

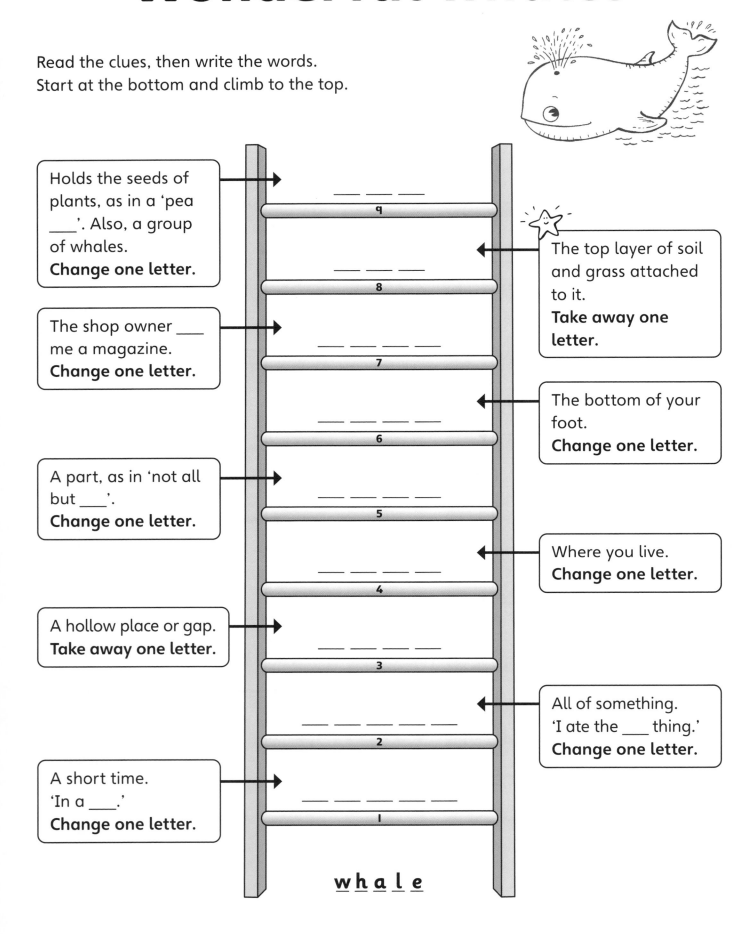

Holds the seeds of plants, as in a 'pea ___'. Also, a group of whales.
Change one letter.

9 __ __ __

The top layer of soil and grass attached to it.
Take away one letter.

8 __ __ __

The shop owner ___ me a magazine.
Change one letter.

7 __ __ __ __

The bottom of your foot.
Change one letter.

6 __ __ __ __

A part, as in 'not all but ___'.
Change one letter.

5 __ __ __ __

Where you live.
Change one letter.

4 __ __ __ __

A hollow place or gap.
Take away one letter.

3 __ __ __ __

All of something. 'I ate the ___ thing.'
Change one letter.

2 __ __ __ __ __

A short time. 'In a ___.'
Change one letter.

1 __ __ __ __ __

w h a l e

Daily Word Ladders for Fluency ■SCHOLASTIC

Name _____

Friendship

Read the clues, then write the words.
Start at the bottom and climb to the top.

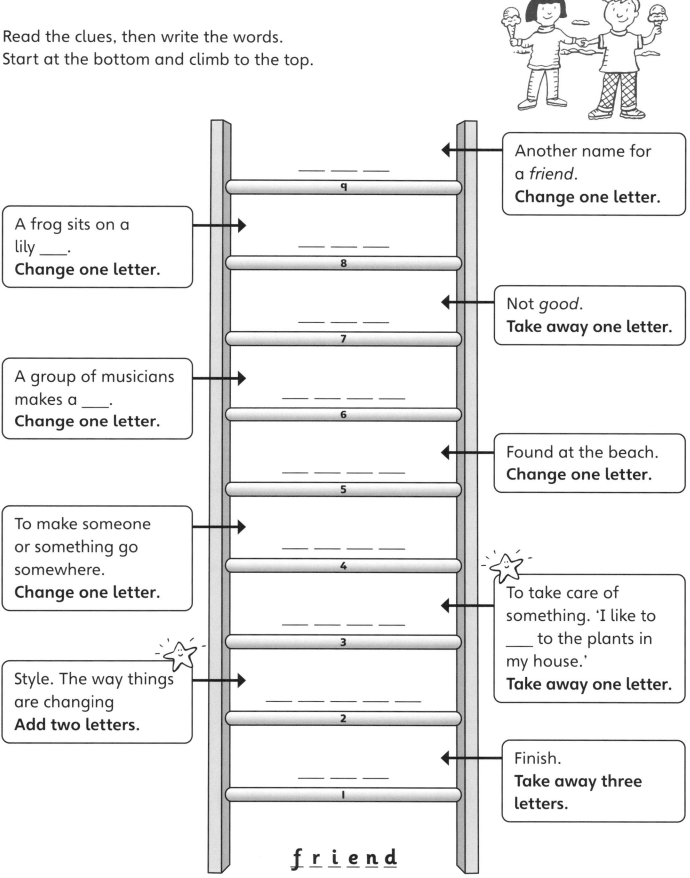

Another name for a *friend*.
Change one letter.

A frog sits on a lily ___.
Change one letter.

Not *good*.
Take away one letter.

A group of musicians makes a ___.
Change one letter.

Found at the beach.
Change one letter.

To make someone or something go somewhere.
Change one letter.

To take care of something. 'I like to ___ to the plants in my house.'
Take away one letter.

Style. The way things are changing
Add two letters.

Finish.
Take away three letters.

9

8

7

6

5

4

3

2

1

f r i e n d

Name _____

Great grapes

Read the clues, then write the words.
Start at the bottom and climb to the top.

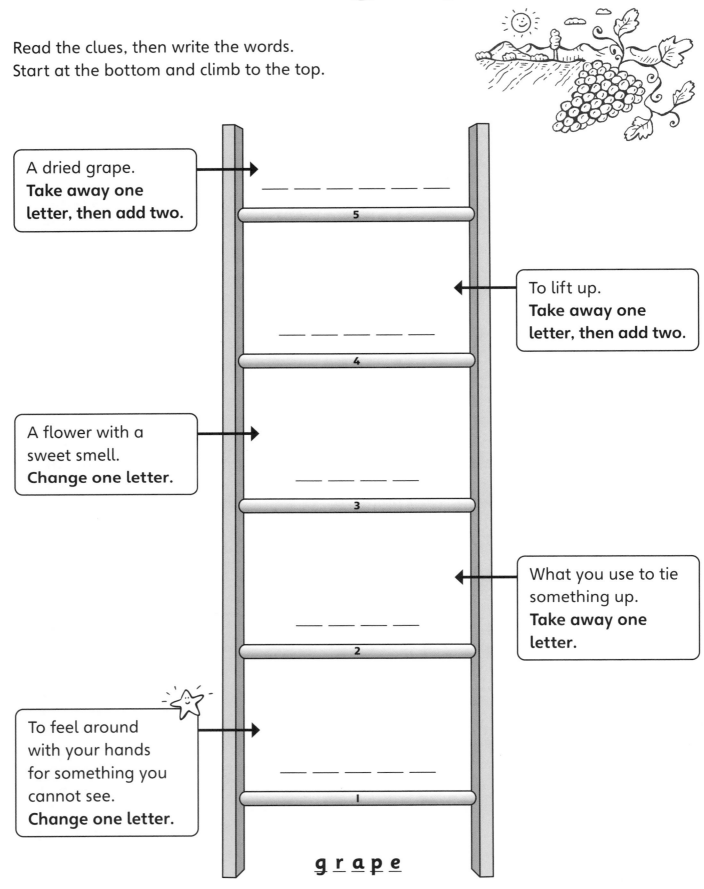

A dried grape.
Take away one letter, then add two.

To lift up.
Take away one letter, then add two.

A flower with a sweet smell.
Change one letter.

What you use to tie something up.
Take away one letter.

To feel around with your hands for something you cannot see.
Change one letter.

5

4

3

2

1

g r a p e

Daily Word Ladders for Fluency **SCHOLASTIC**

Name _____

Busy bees

Read the clues, then write the words.
Start at the bottom and climb to the top.

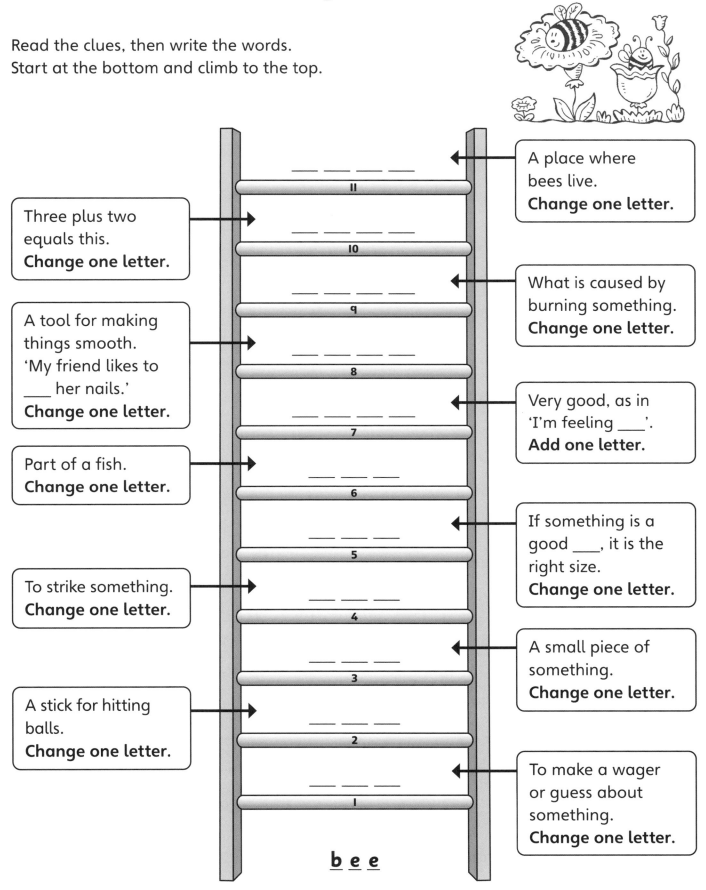

Three plus two equals this. Change one letter. → 10

A tool for making things smooth. 'My friend likes to ___ her nails.' Change one letter. → 8

Part of a fish. Change one letter. → 6

To strike something. Change one letter. → 4

A stick for hitting balls. Change one letter. → 2

A place where bees live. **Change one letter.** ← 11

What is caused by burning something. **Change one letter.** ← 9

Very good, as in 'I'm feeling ___'. **Add one letter.** ← 7

If something is a good ___, it is the right size. **Change one letter.** ← 5

A small piece of something. **Change one letter.** ← 3

To make a wager or guess about something. **Change one letter.** ← 1

b e e

Name _____

Personality change

Read the clues, then write the words.
Start at the bottom and climb to the top.

Not *nice*.
Add one letter.

More than one man.
Change one letter.

The material at the back of a goal to catch the football; a fishing ___.
Take away the first and last letters, then add one vowel.

3 + 3 + 4 =
Rearrange the letters.

'I put my hand ___ my glove'
Take away the first two letters, then add a vowel at the end.

To show someone something by extending your finger.
Add one letter.

An amount of liquid. Often used for milk.
Change one letter.

A herb with green leaves; sometimes used in tea.
Change one letter.

If it belongs to me, it is ___.
Change one letter.

More than one mouse.
Change one letter.

10
9
8
7
6
5
4
3
2
1

n i c e

Daily Word Ladders for Fluency **SCHOLASTIC**

Name _____

Ride 'em

Read the clues, then write the words.
Start at the bottom and climb to the top.

A place where ships load and unload cargo.
Change two letters.

A place with grass and trees.
Add one letter.

Opposite of *peace*.
Take away one letter.

A small animal that lives in the soil.
Take away two letters, then add one.

A small horse.
Change two letters.

If you ___ up, you become more cheerful.
Change one letter.

The score golfers expect on each hole of a golf game.
Change one letter.

Hot, but not too hot.
Change one letter.

More than bad.
Change one letter.

9 __ __ __ __ __

8 __ __ __ __ __

7 __ __ __ __ __

6 __ __ __ __ __

5 __ __ __ __

4 __ __ __ __

3 __ __ __ __ __

2 __ __ __ __ __

1 __ __ __ __ __

<u>h</u> <u>o</u> <u>r</u> <u>s</u> <u>e</u>

Name _____

Love life

Read the clues, then write the words.
Start at the bottom and climb to the top.

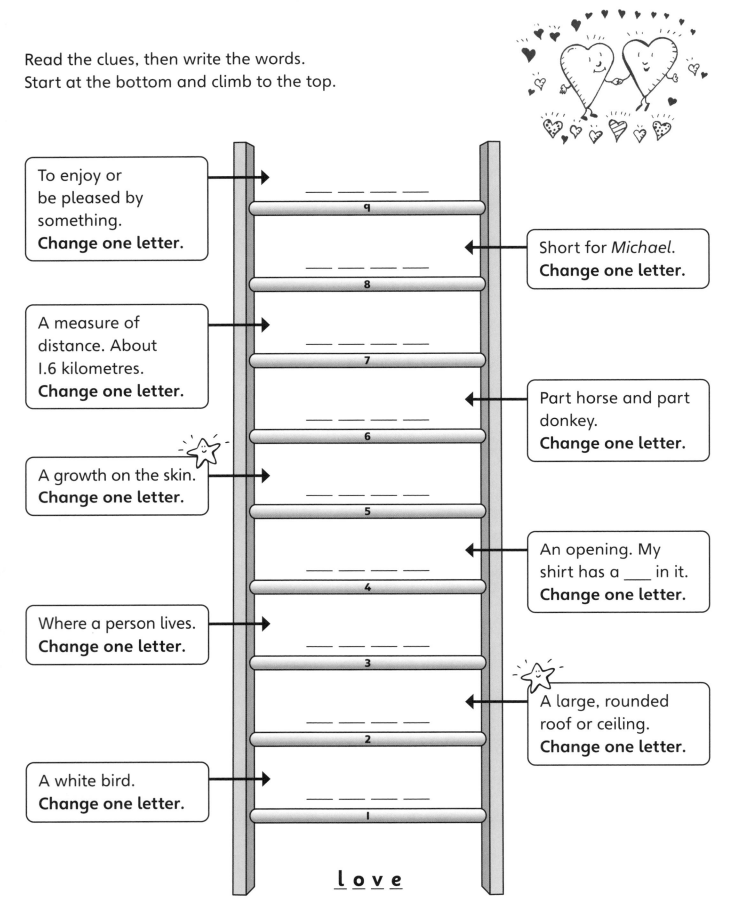

To enjoy or be pleased by something.
Change one letter.
→ 9 _ _ _ _ _

Short for *Michael*.
Change one letter.
8 _ _ _ _ ←

A measure of distance. About 1.6 kilometres.
Change one letter.
→ 7 _ _ _ _

Part horse and part donkey.
Change one letter.
6 _ _ _ _ ←

A growth on the skin.
Change one letter.
→ 5 _ _ _ _

An opening. My shirt has a ___ in it.
Change one letter.
4 _ _ _ _ ←

Where a person lives.
Change one letter.
→ 3 _ _ _ _

A large, rounded roof or ceiling.
Change one letter.
2 _ _ _ _ ←

A white bird.
Change one letter.
→ 1 _ _ _ _

<u>l</u> <u>o</u> <u>v</u> <u>e</u>

Daily Word Ladders for Fluency **SCHOLASTIC**

Underfoot

Read the clues, then write the words.
Start at the bottom and climb to the top.

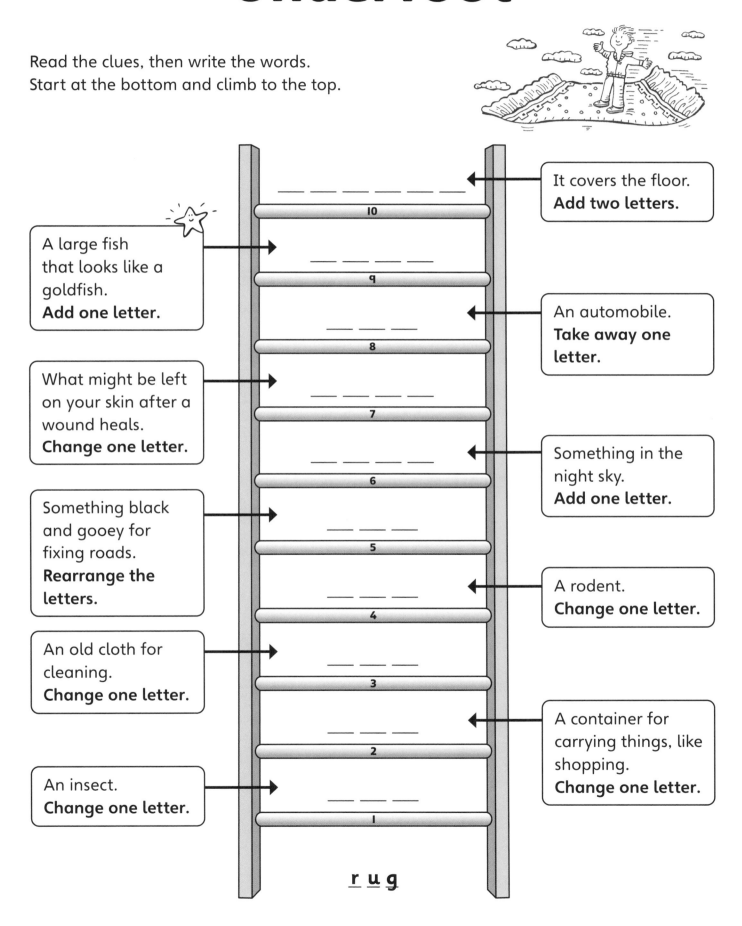

It covers the floor.
Add two letters.

10 _ _ _ _ _ _ _

A large fish that looks like a goldfish.
Add one letter.

9 _ _ _ _

An automobile.
Take away one letter.

8 _ _ _

What might be left on your skin after a wound heals.
Change one letter.

7 _ _ _ _

Something in the night sky.
Add one letter.

6 _ _ _ _ _

Something black and gooey for fixing roads.
Rearrange the letters.

5 _ _ _

A rodent.
Change one letter.

4 _ _ _

An old cloth for cleaning.
Change one letter.

3 _ _ _

A container for carrying things, like shopping.
Change one letter.

2 _ _ _ _

An insect.
Change one letter.

1 _ _ _ _

r u g

Name _____

Bare feet

Read the clues, then write the words.
Start at the bottom and climb to the top.

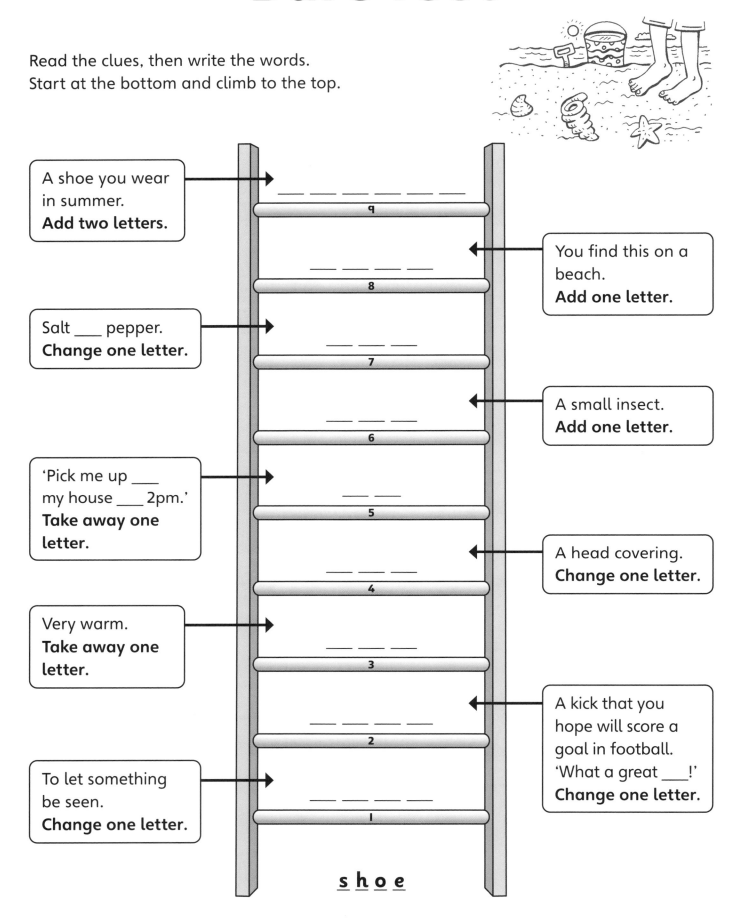

A shoe you wear in summer. **Add two letters.** → 9 _ _ _ _ _ _

_ _ _ _ _ 8 ← You find this on a beach. **Add one letter.**

Salt ___ pepper. **Change one letter.** → 7 _ _ _

_ _ _ _ 6 ← A small insect. **Add one letter.**

'Pick me up ___ my house ___ 2pm.' **Take away one letter.** → 5 _ _

_ _ _ _ 4 ← A head covering. **Change one letter.**

Very warm. **Take away one letter.** → 3 _ _ _ _

_ _ _ _ 2 ← A kick that you hope will score a goal in football. 'What a great ___!' **Change one letter.**

To let something be seen. **Change one letter.** → 1 _ _ _ _

s h o e

Daily Word Ladders for Fluency ■SCHOLASTIC

Name _____

Colour change

Read the clues, then write the words.
Start at the bottom and climb to the top.

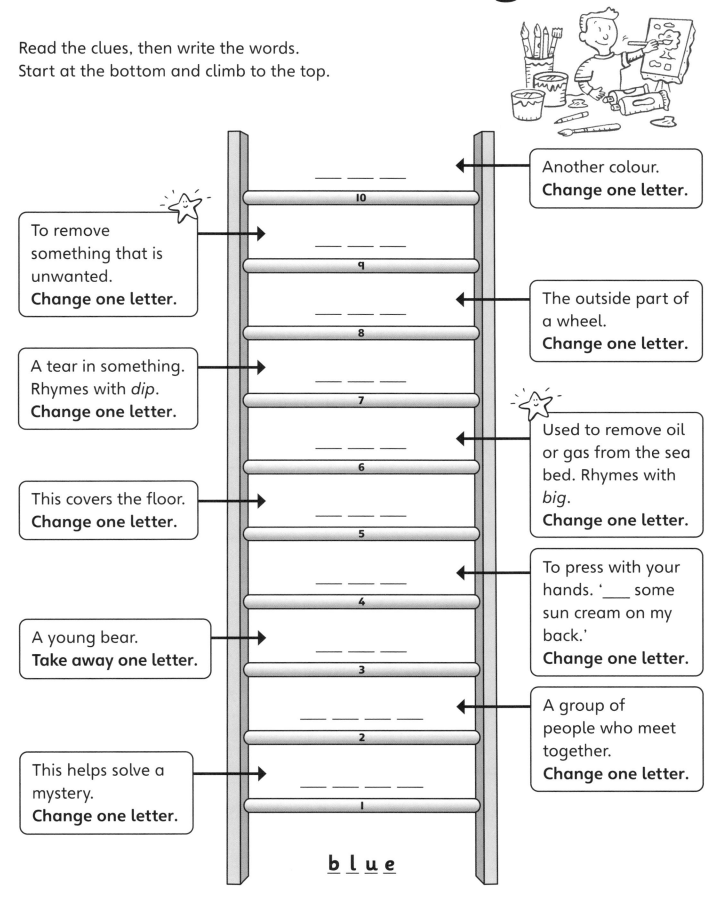

Another colour.
Change one letter.

To remove something that is unwanted.
Change one letter.

The outside part of a wheel.
Change one letter.

A tear in something. Rhymes with *dip*.
Change one letter.

Used to remove oil or gas from the sea bed. Rhymes with *big*.
Change one letter.

This covers the floor.
Change one letter.

To press with your hands. '___ some sun cream on my back.'
Change one letter.

A young bear.
Take away one letter.

A group of people who meet together.
Change one letter.

This helps solve a mystery.
Change one letter.

b l u e

10
9
8
7
6
5
4
3
2
1

Deep freeze

Read the clues, then write the words.
Start at the bottom and climb to the top.

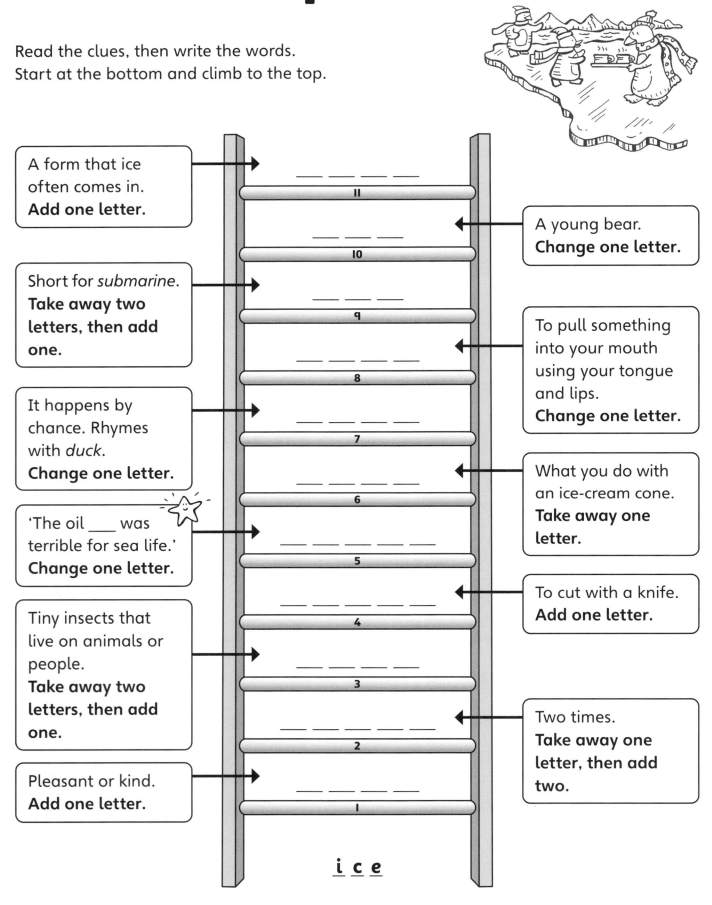

A form that ice often comes in. **Add one letter.**

11 _ _ _ _ _

A young bear. **Change one letter.**

10 _ _ _ _

Short for *submarine*. **Take away two letters, then add one.**

9 _ _ _ _

To pull something into your mouth using your tongue and lips. **Change one letter.**

8 _ _ _ _ _

It happens by chance. Rhymes with *duck*. **Change one letter.**

7 _ _ _ _

What you do with an ice-cream cone. **Take away one letter.**

6 _ _ _ _

'The oil ___ was terrible for sea life.' **Change one letter.**

5 _ _ _ _ _

To cut with a knife. **Add one letter.**

4 _ _ _ _ _

Tiny insects that live on animals or people. **Take away two letters, then add one.**

3 _ _ _ _

Two times. **Take away one letter, then add two.**

2 _ _ _ _ _

Pleasant or kind. **Add one letter.**

1 _ _ _ _

i c e

Daily Word Ladders for Fluency **SCHOLASTIC**

Name _____

In the kitchen

Read the clues, then write the words.
Start at the bottom and climb to the top.

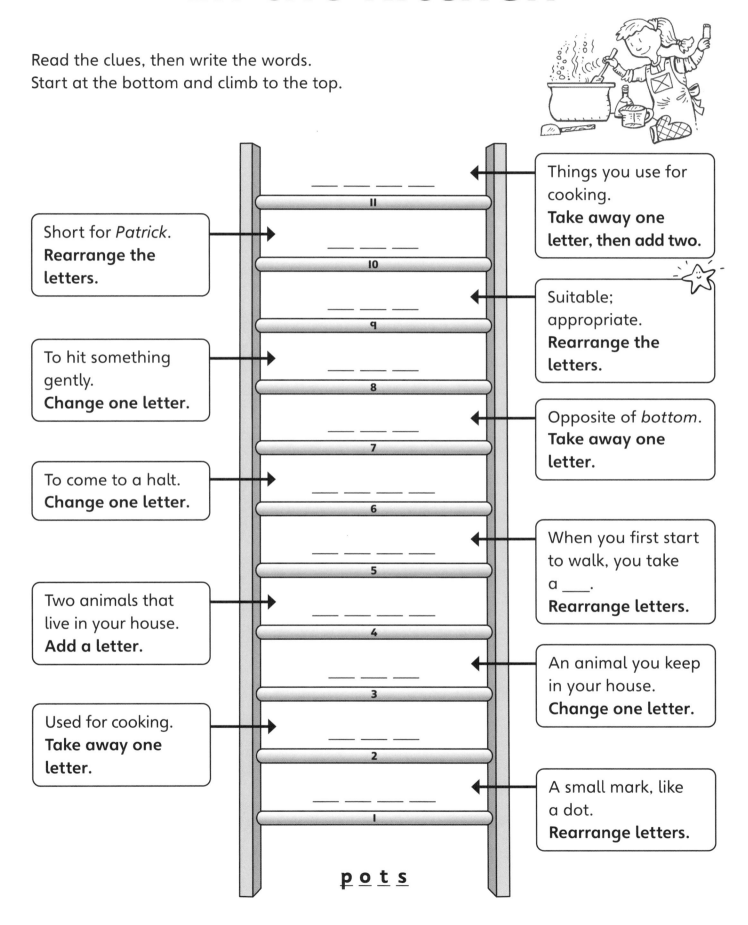

11. _ _ _ _ _

Things you use for cooking. **Take away one letter, then add two.**

Short for *Patrick*. **Rearrange the letters.**

10. _ _ _ _

Suitable; appropriate. **Rearrange the letters.**

9. _ _ _ _

To hit something gently. **Change one letter.**

8. _ _ _ _

Opposite of *bottom*. **Take away one letter.**

7. _ _ _ _

To come to a halt. **Change one letter.**

6. _ _ _ _

5. _ _ _ _

When you first start to walk, you take a ___. **Rearrange letters.**

Two animals that live in your house. **Add a letter.**

4. _ _ _ _

3. _ _ _

An animal you keep in your house. **Change one letter.**

Used for cooking. **Take away one letter.**

2. _ _ _ _

1. _ _ _ _

A small mark, like a dot. **Rearrange letters.**

p o t s

Being grateful

Name _____

Read the clues, then write the words.
Start at the bottom and climb to the top.

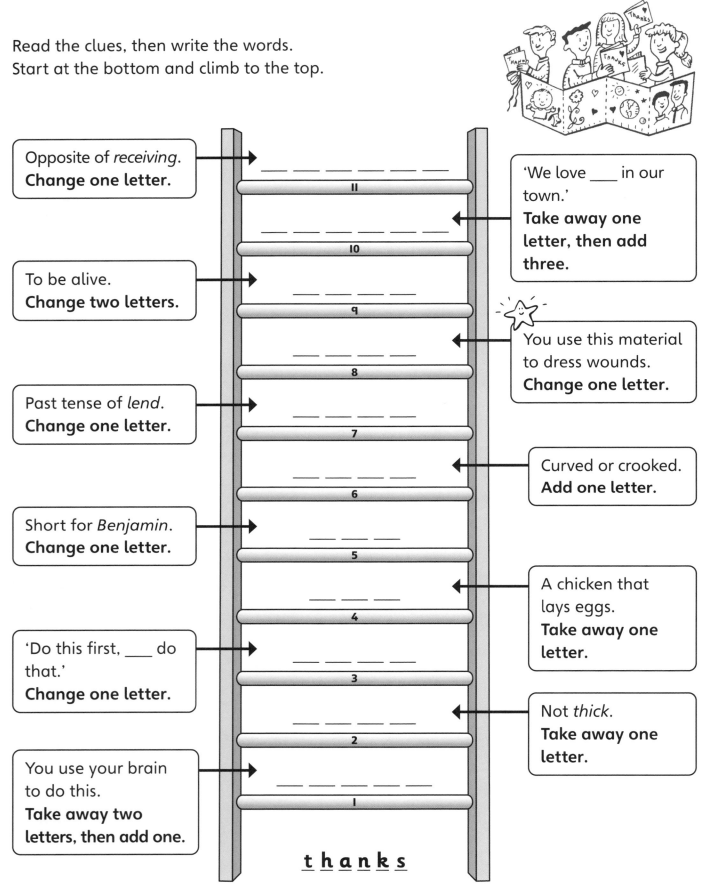

Opposite of *receiving*.
Change one letter.

11 _ _ _ _ _ _

'We love ___ in our town.'
Take away one letter, then add three.

10 _ _ _ _ _ _

To be alive.
Change two letters.

9 _ _ _ _

You use this material to dress wounds.
Change one letter.

8 _ _ _ _

Past tense of *lend*.
Change one letter.

7 _ _ _ _

Curved or crooked.
Add one letter.

6 _ _ _

Short for *Benjamin*.
Change one letter.

5 _ _ _

A chicken that lays eggs.
Take away one letter.

4 _ _ _

'Do this first, ___ do that.'
Change one letter.

3 _ _ _ _

Not *thick*.
Take away one letter.

2 _ _ _ _

You use your brain to do this.
Take away two letters, then add one.

1 _ _ _ _ _

t h a n k s

Photocopiable

Daily Word Ladders for Fluency **SCHOLASTIC**

Name _____

Ship ahoy

Read the clues, then write the words.
Start at the bottom and climb to the top.

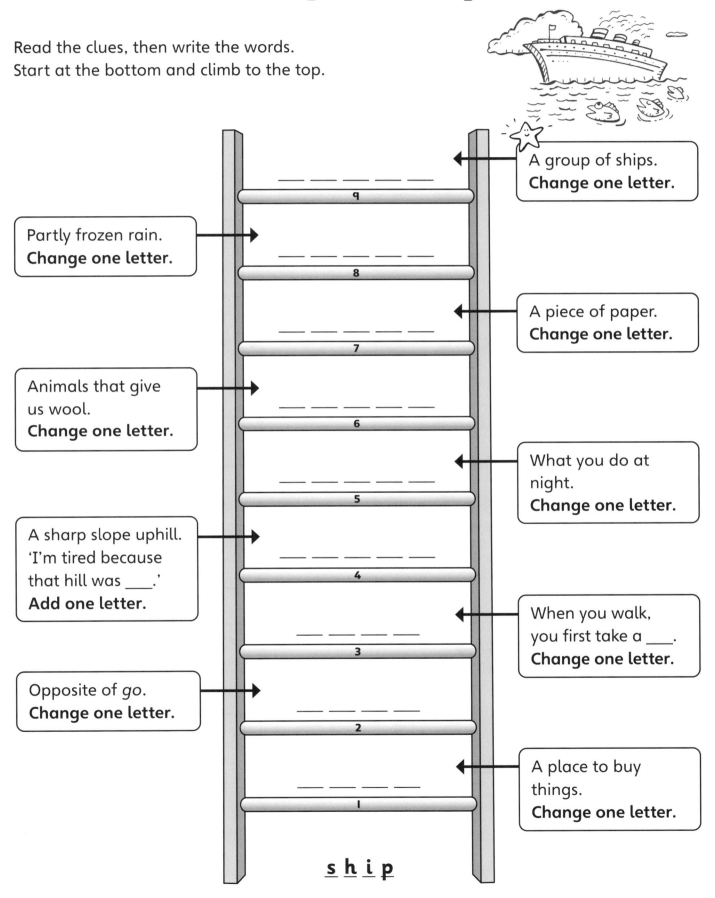

A group of ships.
Change one letter.

Partly frozen rain.
Change one letter.

A piece of paper.
Change one letter.

Animals that give us wool.
Change one letter.

What you do at night.
Change one letter.

A sharp slope uphill. 'I'm tired because that hill was ___.'
Add one letter.

When you walk, you first take a ___.
Change one letter.

Opposite of *go*.
Change one letter.

A place to buy things.
Change one letter.

9

8

7

6

5

4

3

2

1

s h i p

Vehicles

Read the clues, then write the words.
Start at the bottom and climb to the top.

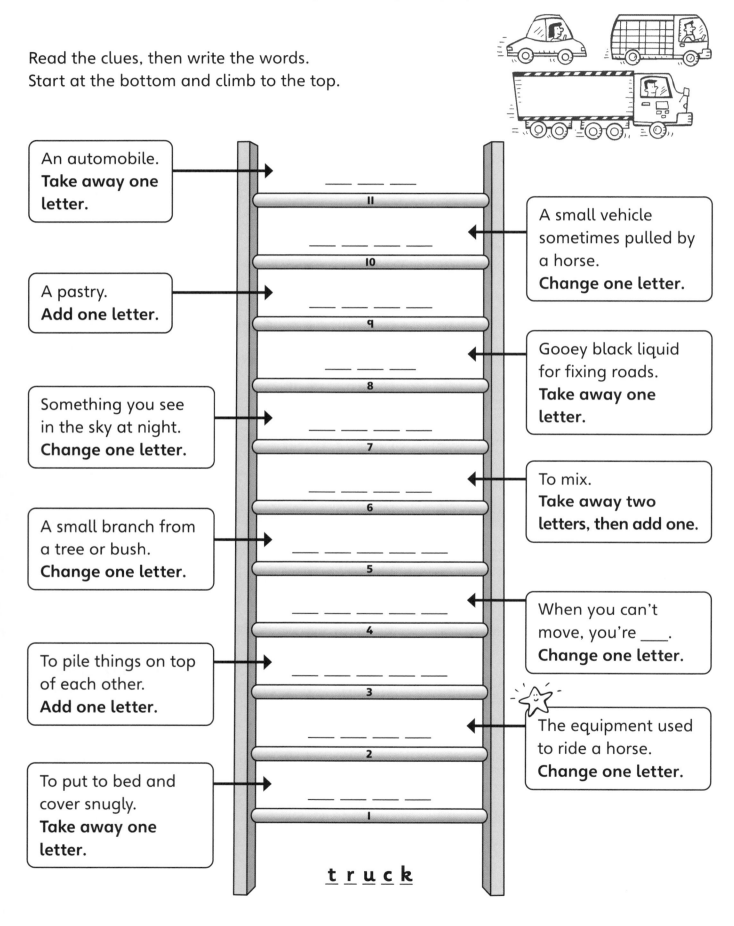

An automobile.
Take away one letter.

— — —
11

A small vehicle sometimes pulled by a horse.
Change one letter.

— — — — —
10

A pastry.
Add one letter.

— — — —
9

Gooey black liquid for fixing roads.
Take away one letter.

— — —
8

Something you see in the sky at night.
Change one letter.

— — — —
7

To mix.
Take away two letters, then add one.

— — — —
6

A small branch from a tree or bush.
Change one letter.

— — — — —
5

When you can't move, you're ___.
Change one letter.

— — — — —
4

To pile things on top of each other.
Add one letter.

— — — —
3

The equipment used to ride a horse.
Change one letter.

— — — —
2

To put to bed and cover snugly.
Take away one letter.

— — — —
1

<u>t</u> <u>r</u> <u>u</u> <u>c</u> <u>k</u>

Name _____

Hungry

Read the clues, then write the words.
Start at the bottom and climb to the top.

The meal you eat in the evening. **Add three letters.**

Loud noise. **Change one letter.**

A place to put rubbish. **Change one letter.**

You put a hot dog in a ___. **Change one letter.**

To forbid something. **Take away one letter.**

A place to save money. **Change one letter.**

A bed stacked on top of another. **Take away two letters, then add one.**

A group of things. A ____ of flowers. **Change one letter.**

8

7

6

5

4

3

2

1

l u n c h

Name _____

Opposites attract 2

Read the clues, then write the words.
Start at the bottom and climb to the top.

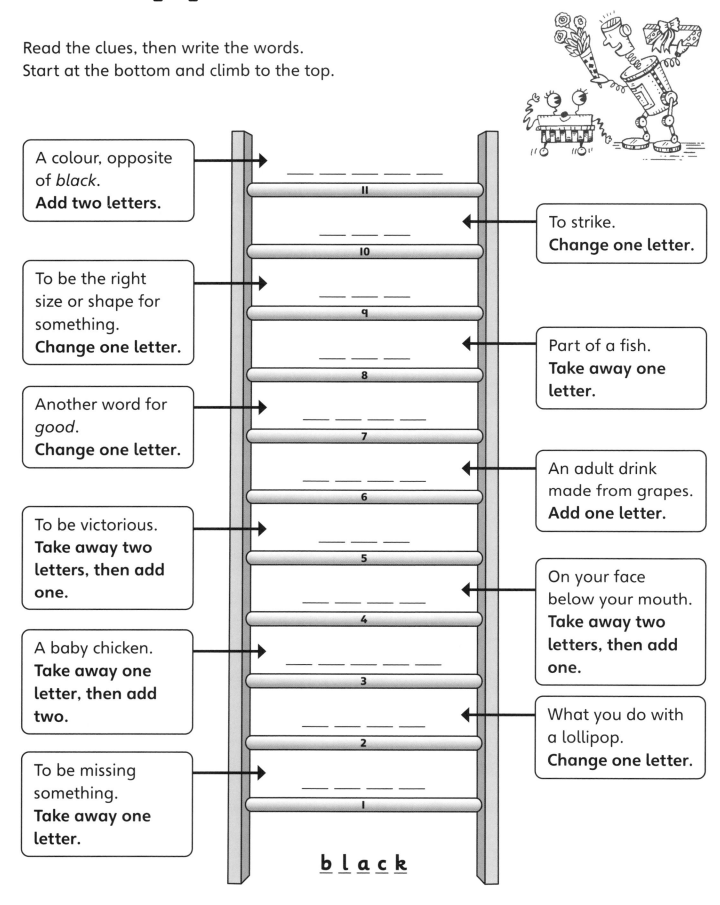

A colour, opposite of *black*.
Add two letters.

To strike.
Change one letter.

To be the right size or shape for something.
Change one letter.

Part of a fish.
Take away one letter.

Another word for *good*.
Change one letter.

An adult drink made from grapes.
Add one letter.

To be victorious.
Take away two letters, then add one.

On your face below your mouth.
Take away two letters, then add one.

A baby chicken.
Take away one letter, then add two.

What you do with a lollipop.
Change one letter.

To be missing something.
Take away one letter.

11
10
9
8
7
6
5
4
3
2
1

b l a c k

Daily Word Ladders for Fluency **SCHOLASTIC**

Nap time

Read the clues, then write the words.
Start at the bottom and climb to the top.

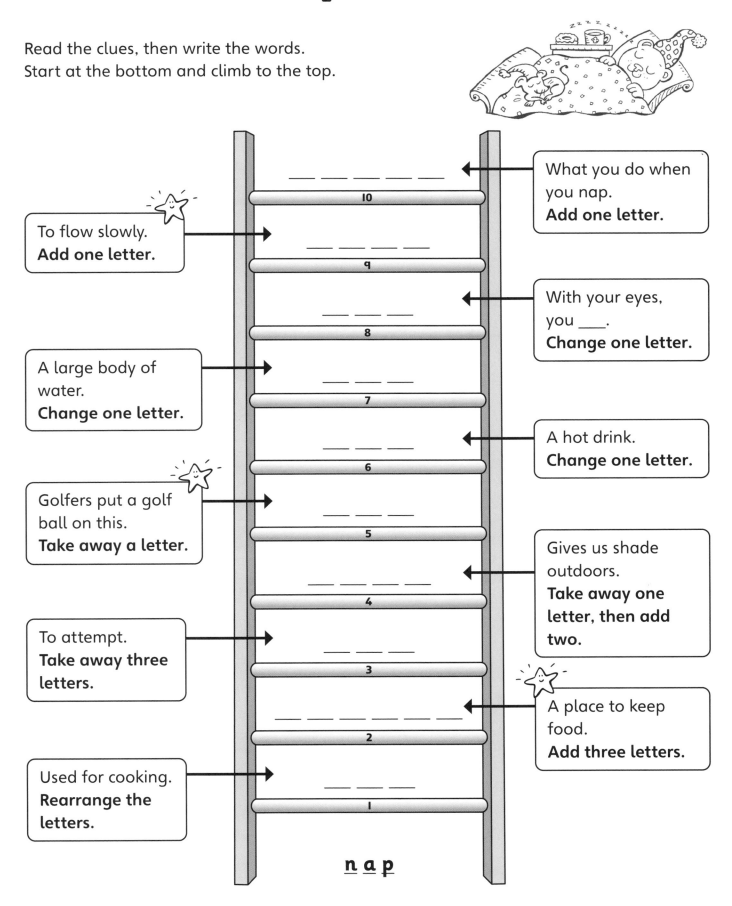

To flow slowly.
Add one letter.

A large body of water.
Change one letter.

Golfers put a golf ball on this.
Take away a letter.

To attempt.
Take away three letters.

Used for cooking.
Rearrange the letters.

10 _ _ _ _ _

9 _ _ _ _ _

8 _ _ _ _

7 _ _ _ _

6 _ _ _ _

5 _ _ _

4 _ _ _ _

3 _ _ _

2 _ _ _ _ _

1 _ _ _

n a p

What you do when you nap.
Add one letter.

With your eyes, you ___.
Change one letter.

A hot drink.
Change one letter.

Gives us shade outdoors.
Take away one letter, then add two.

A place to keep food.
Add three letters.

Name _____

City living

Read the clues, then write the words.
Start at the bottom and climb to the top.

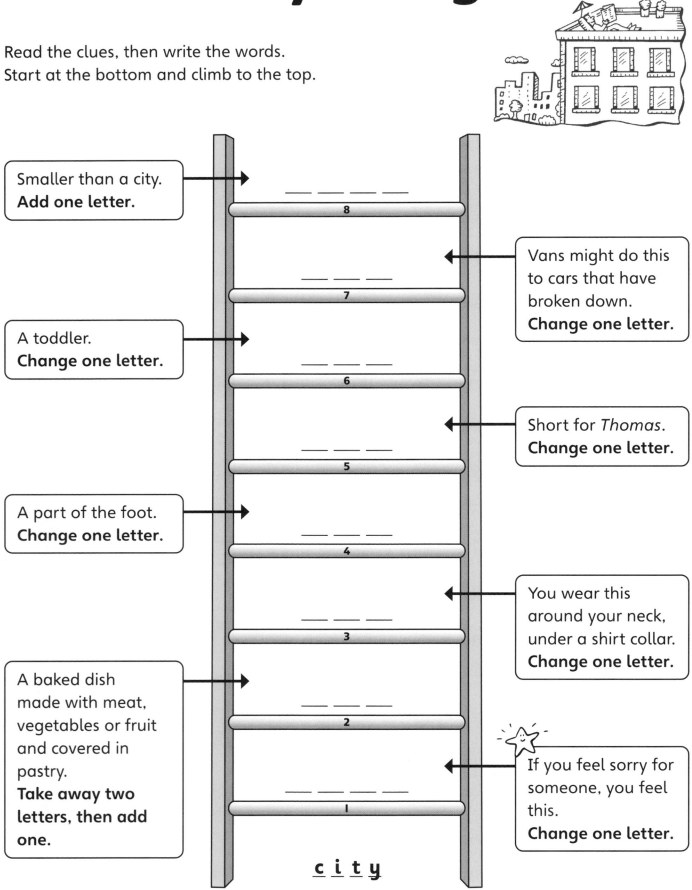

Smaller than a city. **Add one letter.**

— — — — —
8

Vans might do this to cars that have broken down. **Change one letter.**

— — — —
7

A toddler. **Change one letter.**

— — —
6

Short for *Thomas*. **Change one letter.**

— — —
5

A part of the foot. **Change one letter.**

— — — —
4

You wear this around your neck, under a shirt collar. **Change one letter.**

— — — —
3

A baked dish made with meat, vegetables or fruit and covered in pastry. **Take away two letters, then add one.**

— — — —
2

If you feel sorry for someone, you feel this. **Change one letter.**

— — — — —
1

c i t y

Daily Word Ladders for Fluency ■SCHOLASTIC

Name _____

Air travel

Read the clues, then write the words.
Start at the bottom and climb to the top.

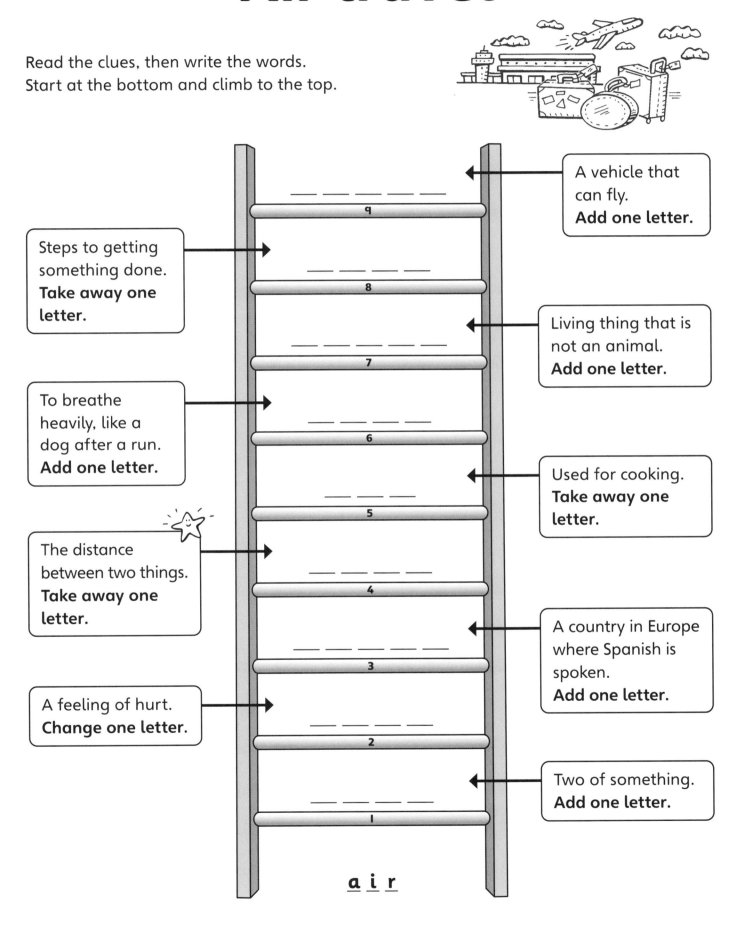

9 — — — — —
A vehicle that can fly. **Add one letter.**

8 — — — — —
Steps to getting something done. **Take away one letter.**

7 — — — — —
Living thing that is not an animal. **Add one letter.**

6 — — — — —
To breathe heavily, like a dog after a run. **Add one letter.**

5 — — — —
Used for cooking. **Take away one letter.**

4 — — — — —
The distance between two things. **Take away one letter.**

3 — — — — — —
A country in Europe where Spanish is spoken. **Add one letter.**

2 — — — — —
A feeling of hurt. **Change one letter.**

1 — — — —
Two of something. **Add one letter.**

<u>a</u> <u>i</u> <u>r</u>

Snack food

Name _____

Read the clues, then write the words.
Start at the bottom and climb to the top.

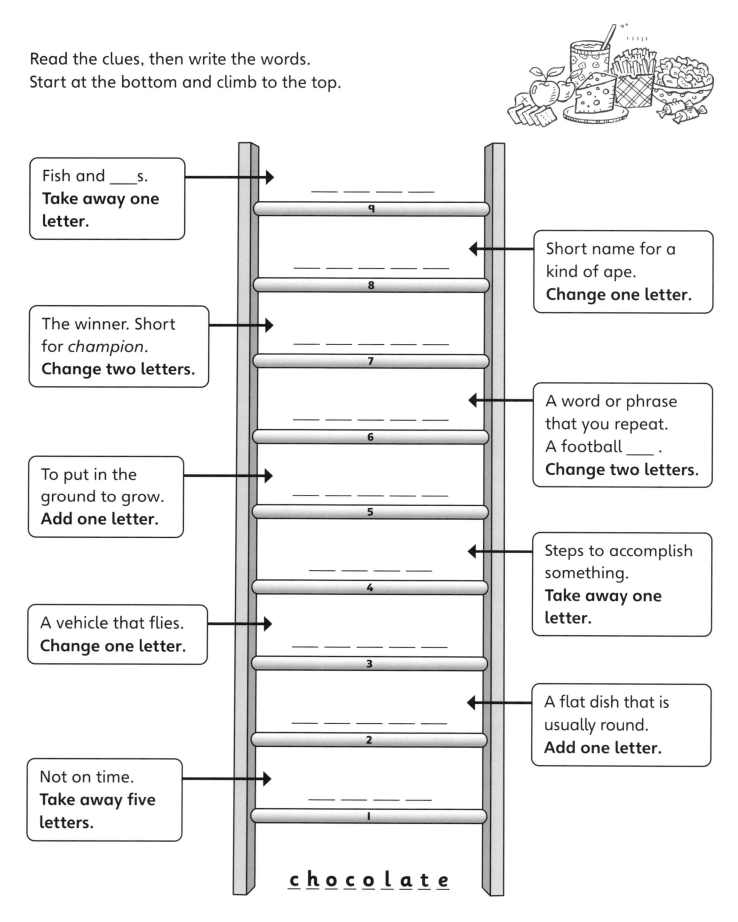

Fish and ___s.
Take away one letter. → (9)

Short name for a kind of ape.
Change one letter. ← (8)

The winner. Short for _champion_.
Change two letters. → (7)

A word or phrase that you repeat. A football ___ .
Change two letters. ← (6)

To put in the ground to grow.
Add one letter. → (5)

Steps to accomplish something.
Take away one letter. ← (4)

A vehicle that flies.
Change one letter. → (3)

A flat dish that is usually round.
Add one letter. ← (2)

Not on time.
Take away five letters. → (1)

c h o c o l a t e

Daily Word Ladders for Fluency ■SCHOLASTIC

Name _____

A matter of size

Read the clues, then write the words.
Start at the bottom and climb to the top.

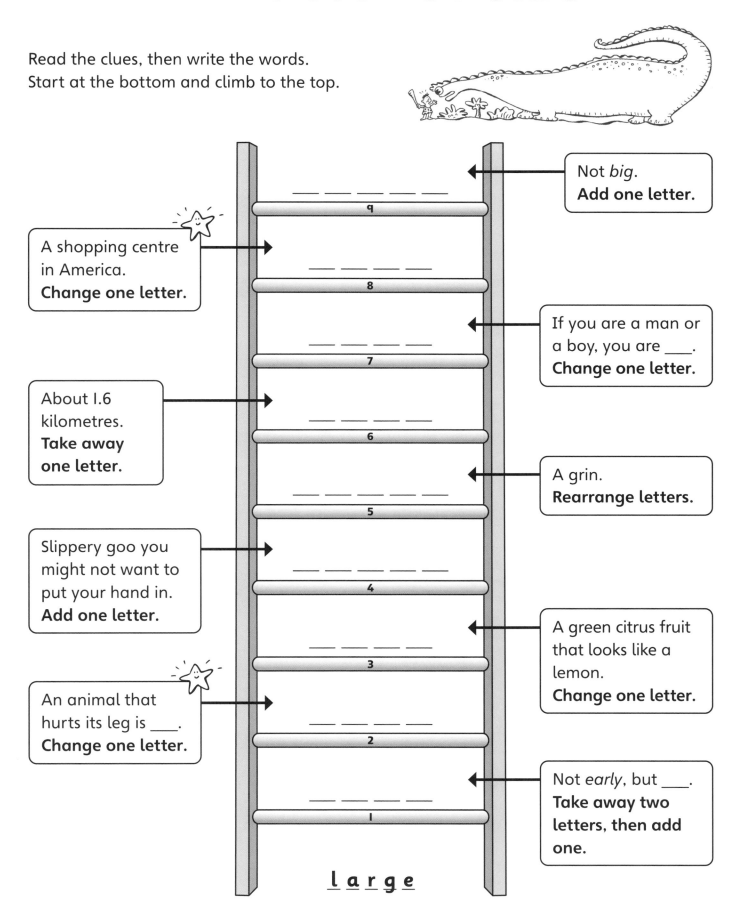

Not *big*.
Add one letter.

A shopping centre in America.
Change one letter.

9 _ _ _ _ _

8 _ _ _ _ _

If you are a man or a boy, you are ___.
Change one letter.

7 _ _ _ _

About 1.6 kilometres.
Take away one letter.

6 _ _ _ _ _

A grin.
Rearrange letters.

5 _ _ _ _ _ _

Slippery goo you might not want to put your hand in.
Add one letter.

4 _ _ _ _ _

A green citrus fruit that looks like a lemon.
Change one letter.

3 _ _ _ _ _

An animal that hurts its leg is ___.
Change one letter.

2 _ _ _ _

Not *early*, but ___.
Take away two letters, then add one.

1 _ _ _ _ _

l a r g e

Name _____

Catnip

Read the clues, then write the words.
Start at the bottom and climb to the top.

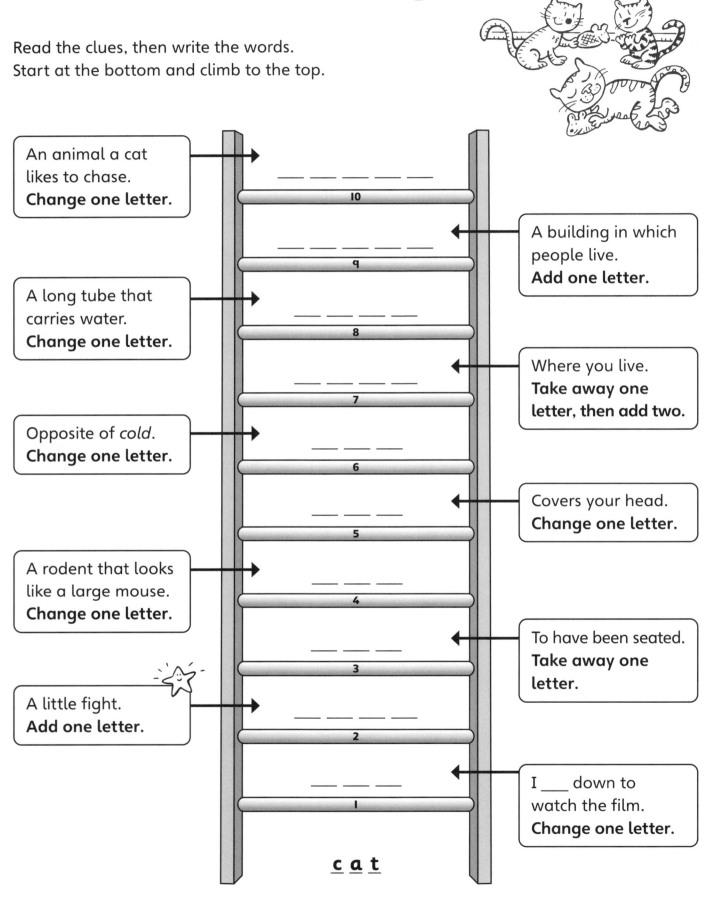

An animal a cat likes to chase.
Change one letter.

A building in which people live.
Add one letter.

A long tube that carries water.
Change one letter.

Where you live.
Take away one letter, then add two.

Opposite of *cold*.
Change one letter.

Covers your head.
Change one letter.

A rodent that looks like a large mouse.
Change one letter.

To have been seated.
Take away one letter.

A little fight.
Add one letter.

I ___ down to watch the film.
Change one letter.

10

9

8

7

6

5

4

3

2

1

<u>c a t</u>

Daily Word Ladders for Fluency ■SCHOLASTIC

Name _____

Showers and flowers

Read the clues, then write the words.
Start at the bottom and climb to the top.

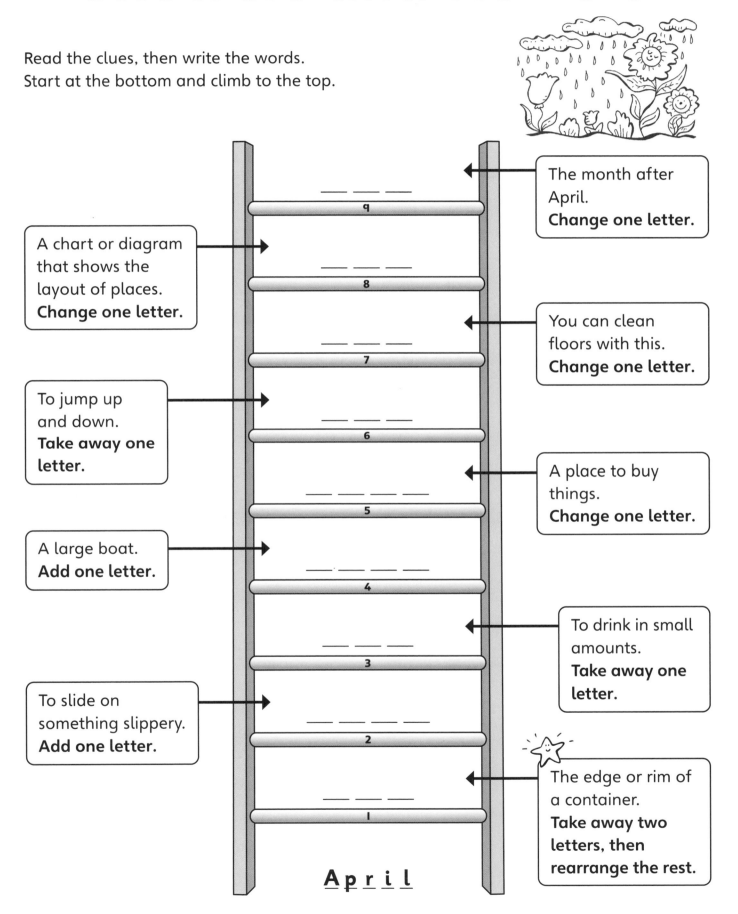

The month after April. **Change one letter.**

A chart or diagram that shows the layout of places. **Change one letter.**

You can clean floors with this. **Change one letter.**

To jump up and down. **Take away one letter.**

A place to buy things. **Change one letter.**

A large boat. **Add one letter.**

To drink in small amounts. **Take away one letter.**

To slide on something slippery. **Add one letter.**

The edge or rim of a container. **Take away two letters, then rearrange the rest.**

A p r i l

Name _____

Coffee break

Read the clues, then write the words.
Start at the bottom and climb to the top.

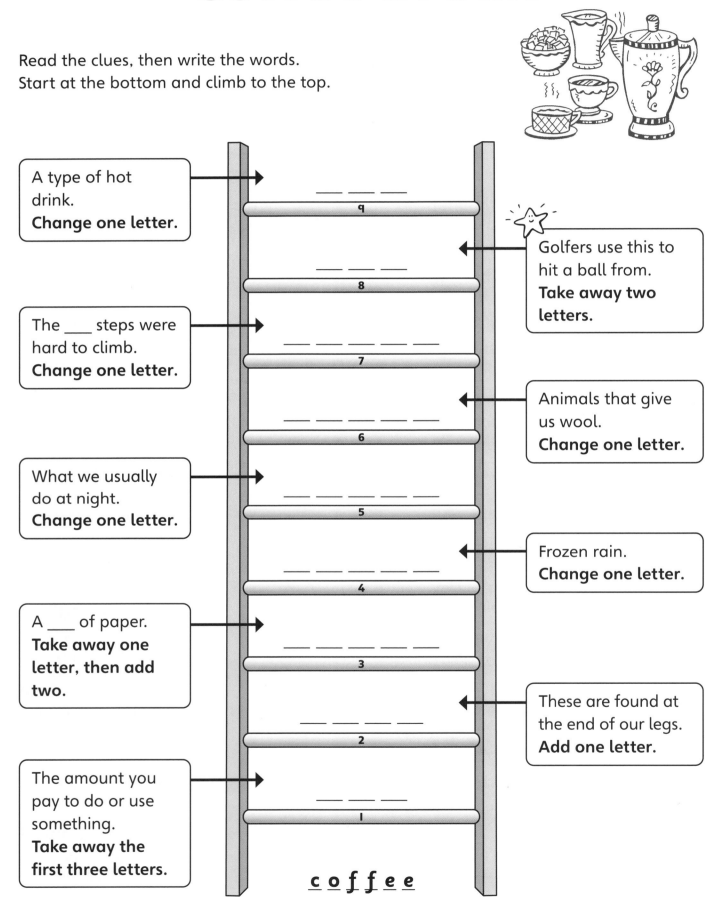

A type of hot drink.
Change one letter.

→ 9 _ _ _ _

8 _ _ _

Golfers use this to hit a ball from. **Take away two letters.** ←

The ___ steps were hard to climb.
Change one letter.

→ 7 _ _ _ _ _

6 _ _ _ _ _ _

Animals that give us wool. **Change one letter.** ←

What we usually do at night.
Change one letter.

→ 5 _ _ _ _ _

4 _ _ _ _ _

Frozen rain. **Change one letter.** ←

A ___ of paper.
Take away one letter, then add two.

→ 3 _ _ _ _ _

2 _ _ _ _

These are found at the end of our legs. **Add one letter.** ←

The amount you pay to do or use something.
Take away the first three letters.

→ 1 _ _ _

c o f f e e

Photocopiable

Daily Word Ladders for Fluency **SCHOLASTIC**

Name _____

Simon says

Read the clues, then write the words.
Start at the bottom and climb to the top.

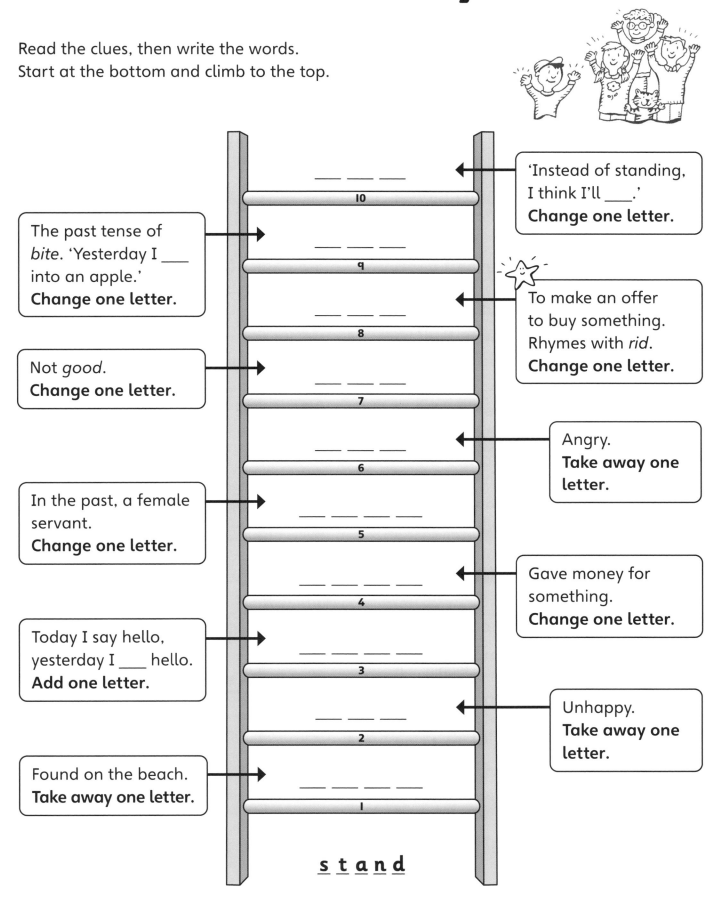

'Instead of standing, I think I'll ____.'
Change one letter.

The past tense of *bite*. 'Yesterday I ____ into an apple.'
Change one letter.

To make an offer to buy something. Rhymes with *rid*.
Change one letter.

Not *good*.
Change one letter.

Angry.
Take away one letter.

In the past, a female servant.
Change one letter.

Gave money for something.
Change one letter.

Today I say hello, yesterday I ____ hello.
Add one letter.

Unhappy.
Take away one letter.

Found on the beach.
Take away one letter.

10
9
8
7
6
5
4
3
2
1

s t a n d

Name _____

Wet and wetter

Read the clues, then write the words.
Start at the bottom and climb to the top.

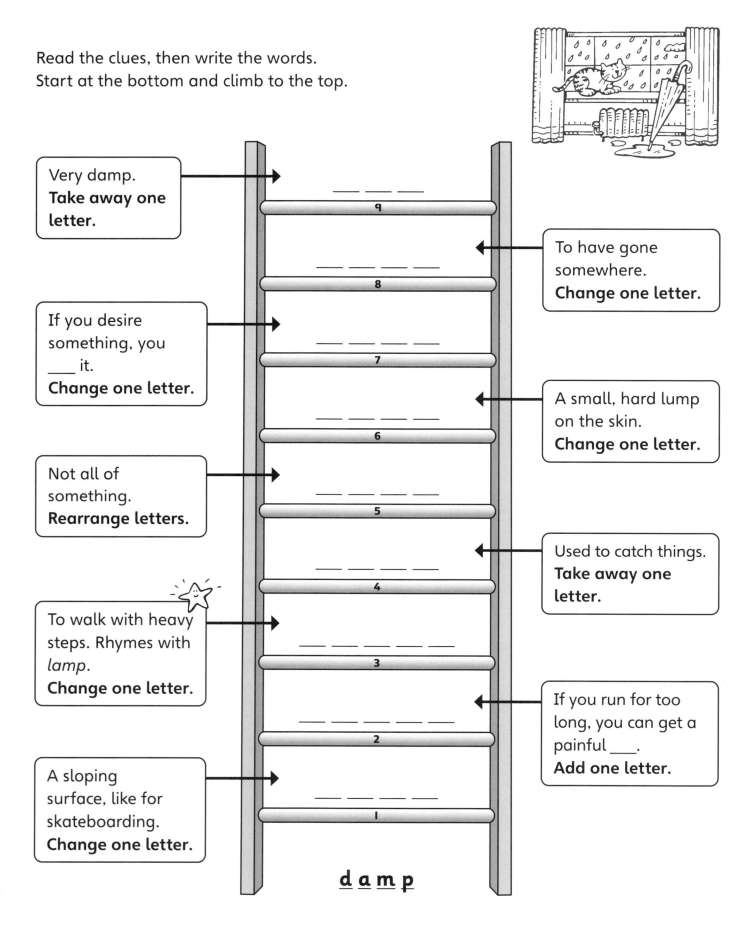

Very damp. **Take away one letter.**

→ 9 ___ ___ ___ ___

← To have gone somewhere. **Change one letter.**

8 ___ ___ ___ ___ ___

If you desire something, you ___ it. **Change one letter.**

→ 7 ___ ___ ___ ___

← A small, hard lump on the skin. **Change one letter.**

6 ___ ___ ___ ___

Not all of something. **Rearrange letters.**

→ 5 ___ ___ ___ ___

← Used to catch things. **Take away one letter.**

4 ___ ___ ___ ___

To walk with heavy steps. Rhymes with *lamp*. **Change one letter.**

→ 3 ___ ___ ___ ___ ___

← If you run for too long, you can get a painful ___. **Add one letter.**

2 ___ ___ ___ ___ ___

A sloping surface, like for skateboarding. **Change one letter.**

→ 1 ___ ___ ___ ___

d a m p

Daily Word Ladders for Fluency ■SCHOLASTIC

After dinner

Read the clues, then write the words.
Start at the bottom and climb to the top.

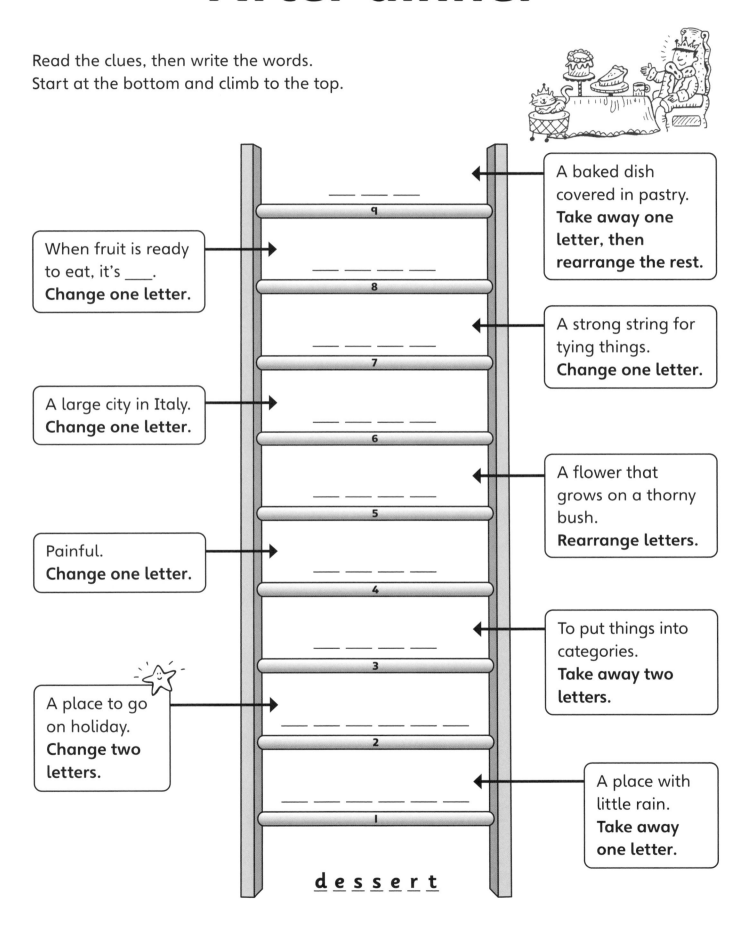

A baked dish covered in pastry. **Take away one letter, then rearrange the rest.**

When fruit is ready to eat, it's ___. **Change one letter.**

A strong string for tying things. **Change one letter.**

A large city in Italy. **Change one letter.**

A flower that grows on a thorny bush. **Rearrange letters.**

Painful. **Change one letter.**

To put things into categories. **Take away two letters.**

A place to go on holiday. **Change two letters.**

A place with little rain. **Take away one letter.**

d e s s e r t

Name _____

Bookworm

Read the clues, then write the words.
Start at the bottom and climb to the top.

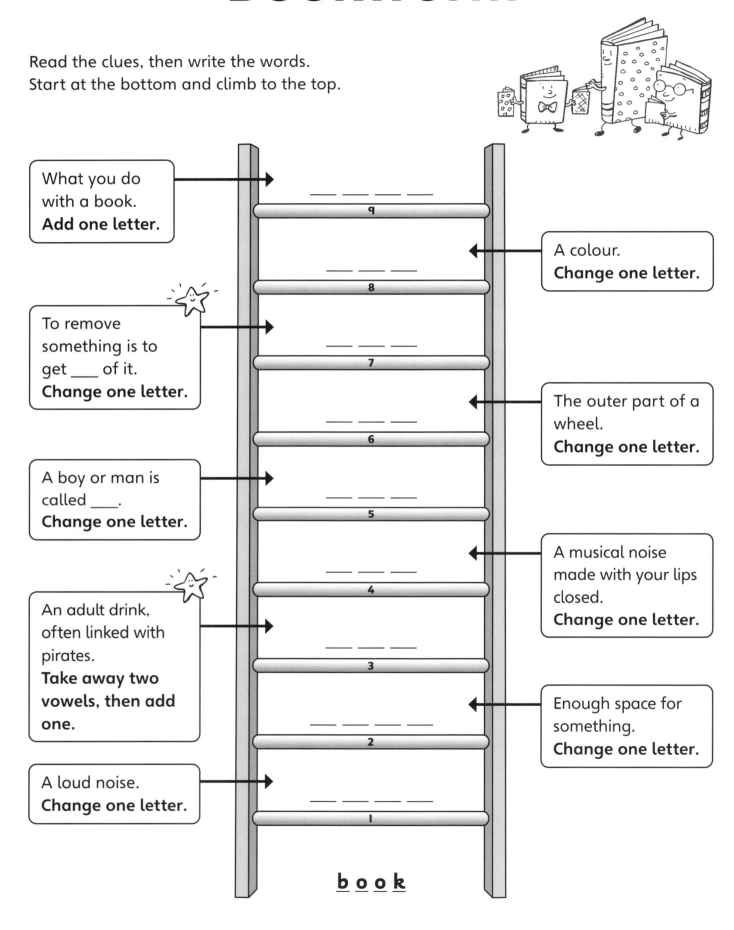

What you do with a book. **Add one letter.**

A colour. **Change one letter.**

To remove something is to get ___ of it. **Change one letter.**

The outer part of a wheel. **Change one letter.**

A boy or man is called ___. **Change one letter.**

A musical noise made with your lips closed. **Change one letter.**

An adult drink, often linked with pirates. **Take away two vowels, then add one.**

Enough space for something. **Change one letter.**

A loud noise. **Change one letter.**

b o o k

Daily Word Ladders for Fluency **SCHOLASTIC**

Name _____

Daily journey

Read the clues, then write the words.
Start at the bottom and climb to the top.

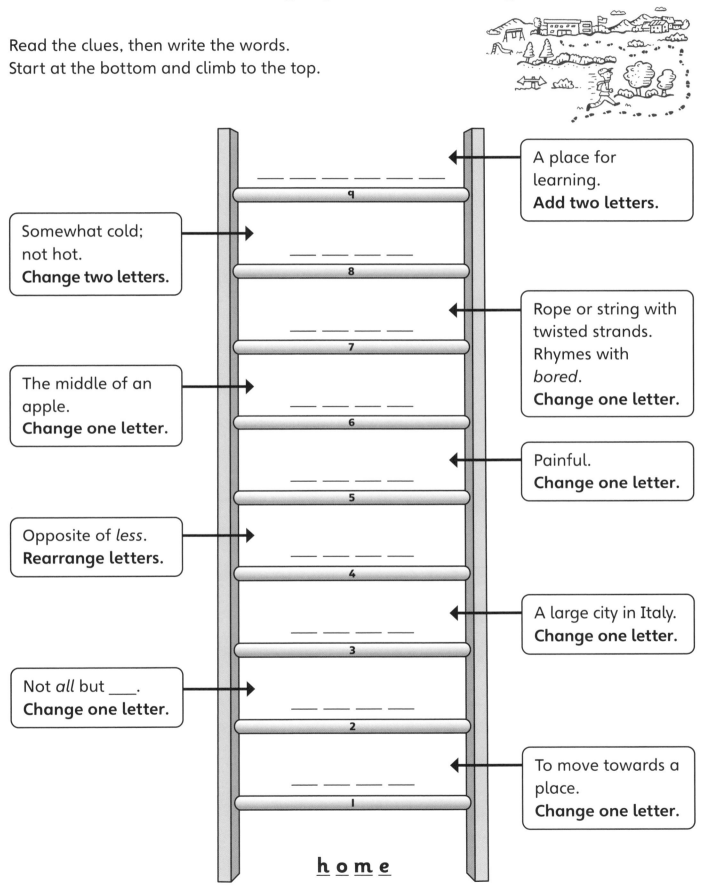

A place for learning. **Add two letters.**

Somewhat cold; not hot. **Change two letters.**

Rope or string with twisted strands. Rhymes with *bored*. **Change one letter.**

The middle of an apple. **Change one letter.**

Painful. **Change one letter.**

Opposite of *less*. **Rearrange letters.**

A large city in Italy. **Change one letter.**

Not *all* but ___. **Change one letter.**

To move towards a place. **Change one letter.**

h o m e

Name _____

Top to bottom

Read the clues, then write the words.
Start at the bottom and climb to the top.

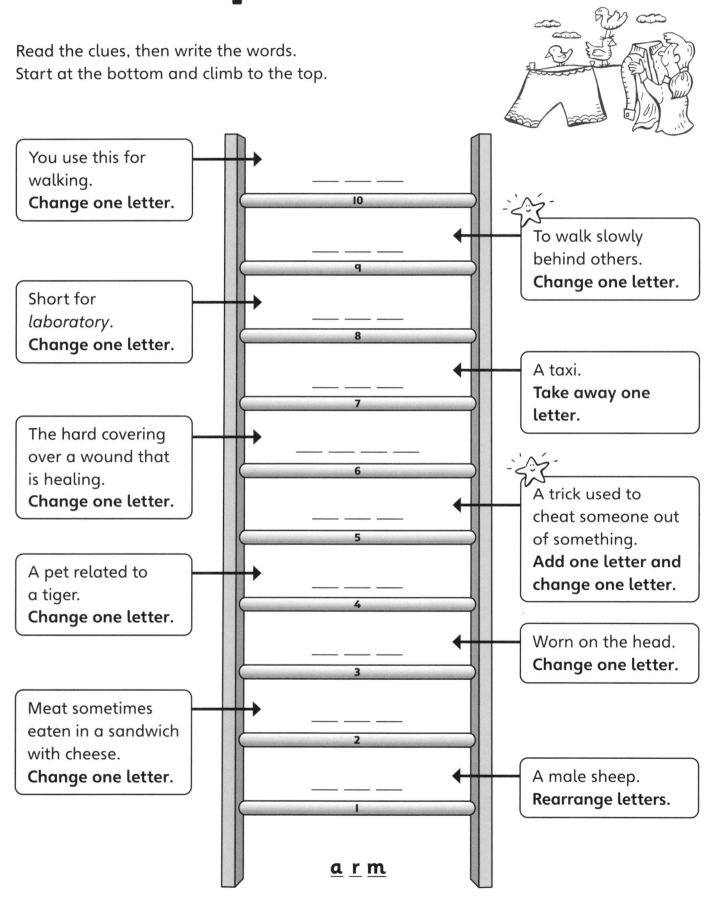

You use this for walking.
Change one letter.

10 ___ ___ ___

To walk slowly behind others.
Change one letter.

9 ___ ___ ___

Short for *laboratory*.
Change one letter.

8 ___ ___ ___

A taxi.
Take away one letter.

7 ___ ___ ___

The hard covering over a wound that is healing.
Change one letter.

6 ___ ___ ___ ___

A trick used to cheat someone out of something.
Add one letter and change one letter.

5 ___ ___ ___

A pet related to a tiger.
Change one letter.

4 ___ ___ ___

Worn on the head.
Change one letter.

3 ___ ___ ___

Meat sometimes eaten in a sandwich with cheese.
Change one letter.

2 ___ ___ ___

A male sheep.
Rearrange letters.

1 <u>a</u> <u>r</u> <u>m</u>

Daily Word Ladders for Fluency **SCHOLASTIC**

Name _____

Finders keepers

Read the clues, then write the words.
Start at the bottom and climb to the top.

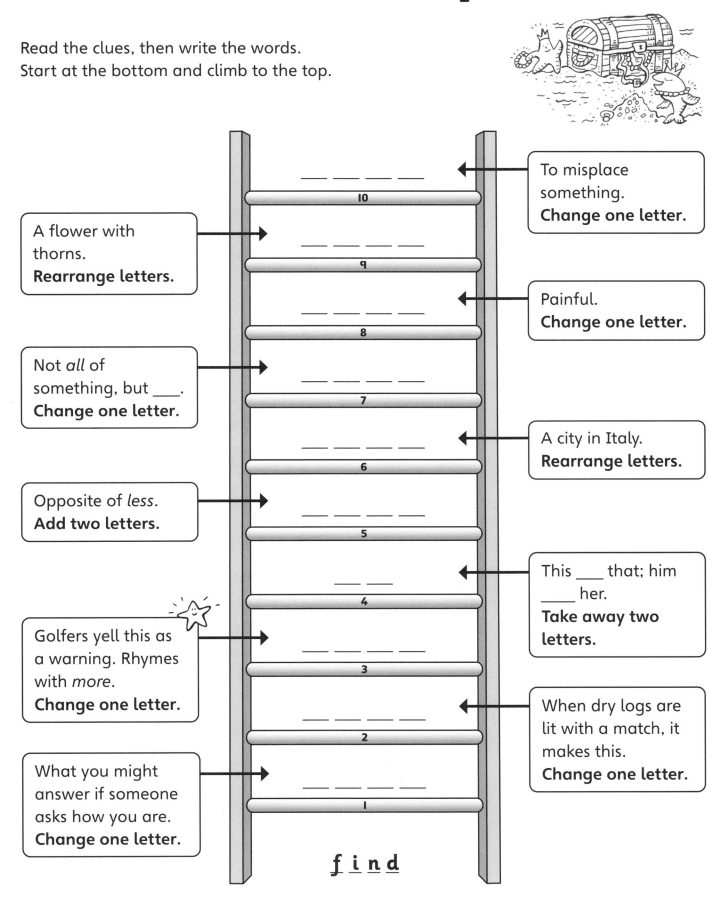

To misplace something. **Change one letter.**

A flower with thorns. **Rearrange letters.**

Painful. **Change one letter.**

Not *all* of something, but ___. **Change one letter.**

A city in Italy. **Rearrange letters.**

Opposite of *less*. **Add two letters.**

This ___ that; him ___ her. **Take away two letters.**

Golfers yell this as a warning. Rhymes with *more*. **Change one letter.**

When dry logs are lit with a match, it makes this. **Change one letter.**

What you might answer if someone asks how you are. **Change one letter.**

f i n d

Tolling time

Read the clues, then write the words.
Start at the bottom and climb to the top.

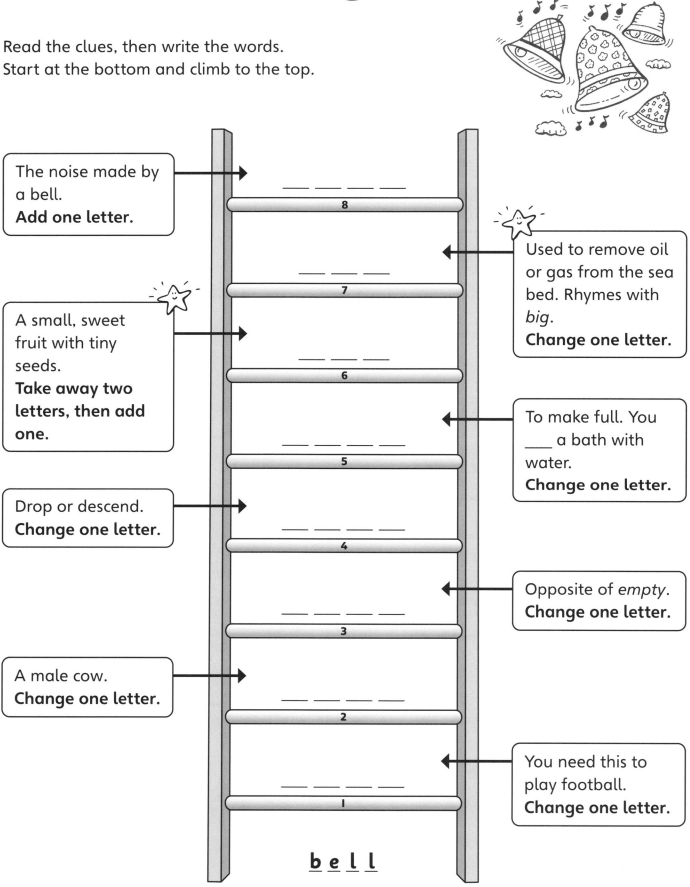

The noise made by a bell.
Add one letter.

Used to remove oil or gas from the sea bed. Rhymes with *big*.
Change one letter.

A small, sweet fruit with tiny seeds.
Take away two letters, then add one.

To make full. You ___ a bath with water.
Change one letter.

Drop or descend.
Change one letter.

Opposite of *empty*.
Change one letter.

A male cow.
Change one letter.

You need this to play football.
Change one letter.

8 _ _ _ _

7 _ _ _

6 _ _ _

5 _ _ _ _

4 _ _ _ _

3 _ _ _ _

2 _ _ _ _

1 _ _ _ _

<u>b</u> <u>e</u> <u>l</u> <u>l</u>

Name _____

Some like it sweet

Read the clues, then write the words.
Start at the bottom and climb to the top.

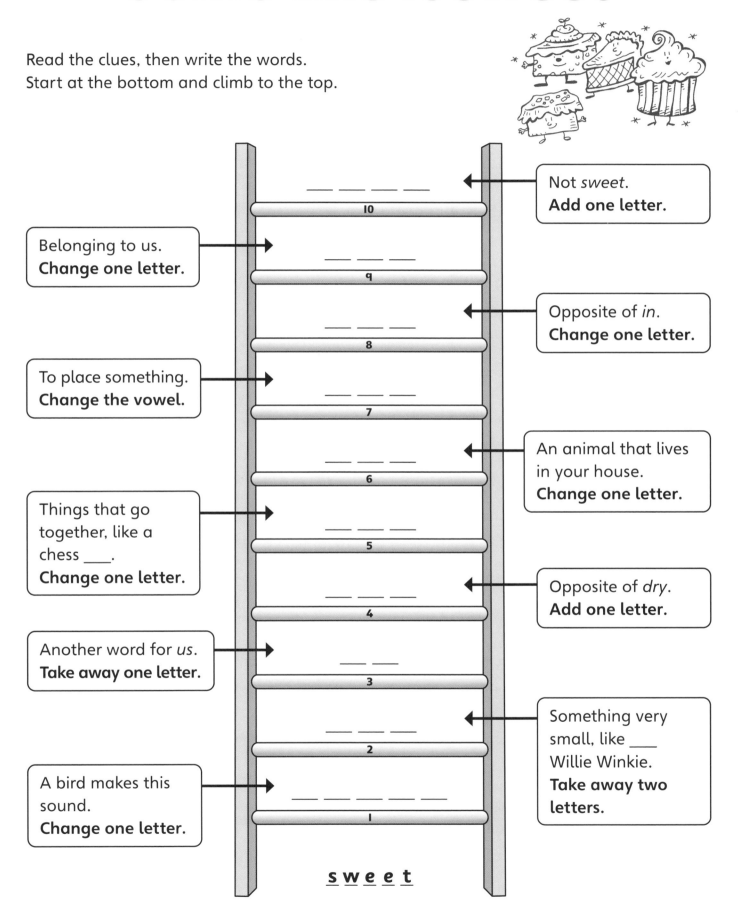

Not *sweet*.
Add one letter.

Belonging to us.
Change one letter.

Opposite of *in*.
Change one letter.

To place something.
Change the vowel.

An animal that lives in your house.
Change one letter.

Things that go together, like a chess ___.
Change one letter.

Opposite of *dry*.
Add one letter.

Another word for *us*.
Take away one letter.

Something very small, like ___ Willie Winkie.
Take away two letters.

A bird makes this sound.
Change one letter.

s w e e t

Name _____

Cricket

Read the clues, then write the words.
Start at the bottom and climb to the top.

Something you play.
Change one letter.
→ 10 _ _ _ _

← Two things that are alike are the ___.
Add one letter.
9 _ _ _ _

Short for *Samuel*.
Change one letter.
→ 8 _ _ _ _

← Meat that comes from a pig.
Change one letter.
7 _ _ _

The edge of a piece of clothing.
Change one letter.
→ 6 _ _ _

← A precious stone.
Change one letter.
5 _ _ _ _

To gain or receive something.
Change one letter.
→ 4 _ _ _

← A wager or guess.
Take away one letter.
3 _ _ _ _

It holds up trousers.
Change one letter.
→ 2 _ _ _ _

← It makes a ringing noise.
Change one letter.
1 _ _ _ _

b a l l

70

Photocopiable

Daily Word Ladders for Fluency ■SCHOLASTIC

Name _____

Good, clean fun

Read the clues, then write the words.
Start at the bottom and climb to the top.

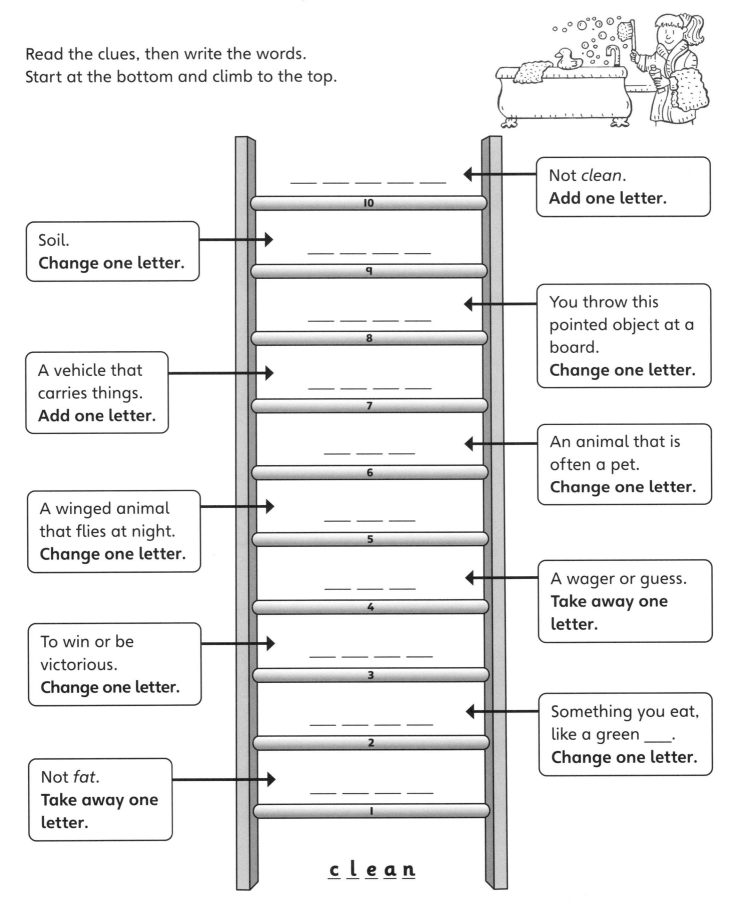

10 — Not *clean*. **Add one letter.**

9 — Soil. **Change one letter.**

8 — You throw this pointed object at a board. **Change one letter.**

7 — A vehicle that carries things. **Add one letter.**

6 — An animal that is often a pet. **Change one letter.**

5 — A winged animal that flies at night. **Change one letter.**

4 — A wager or guess. **Take away one letter.**

3 — To win or be victorious. **Change one letter.**

2 — Something you eat, like a green ___. **Change one letter.**

1 — Not *fat*. **Take away one letter.**

c l e a n

Gently down the stream

Read the clues, then write the words.
Start at the bottom and climb to the top.

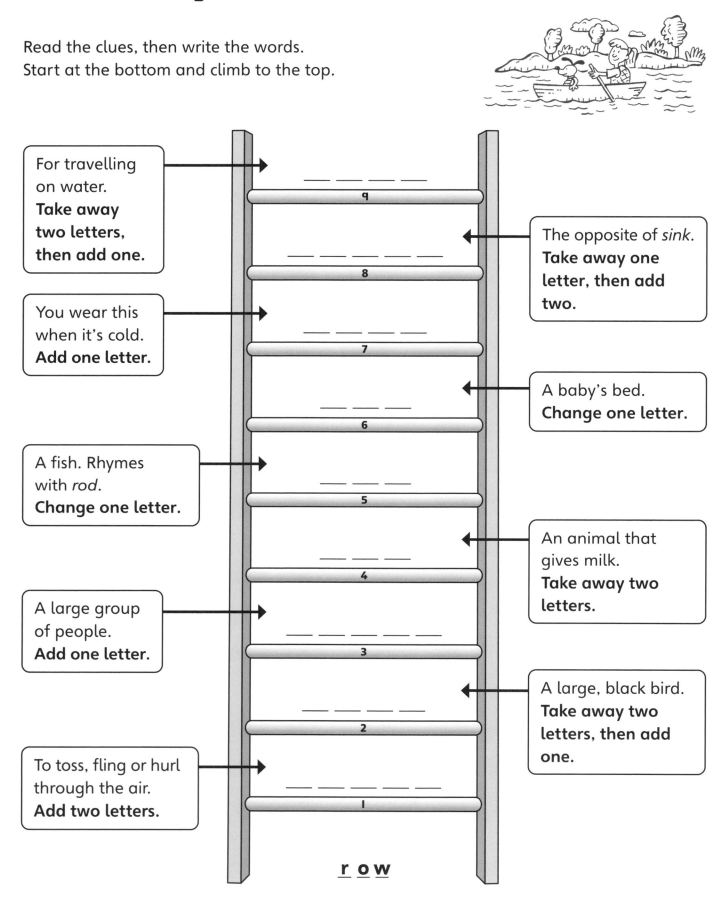

For travelling on water. **Take away two letters, then add one.** → 9 _ _ _ _ _

The opposite of *sink*. **Take away one letter, then add two.** ← 8 _ _ _ _ _ _

You wear this when it's cold. **Add one letter.** → 7 _ _ _ _

A baby's bed. **Change one letter.** ← 6 _ _ _ _

A fish. Rhymes with *rod*. **Change one letter.** → 5 _ _ _ _

An animal that gives milk. **Take away two letters.** ← 4 _ _ _

A large group of people. **Add one letter.** → 3 _ _ _ _ _

A large, black bird. **Take away two letters, then add one.** ← 2 _ _ _ _ _

To toss, fling or hurl through the air. **Add two letters.** → 1 _ _ _ _ _

r o w

Daily Word Ladders for Fluency **SCHOLASTIC**

Name _____

Better and better

Read the clues, then write the words.
Start at the bottom and climb to the top.

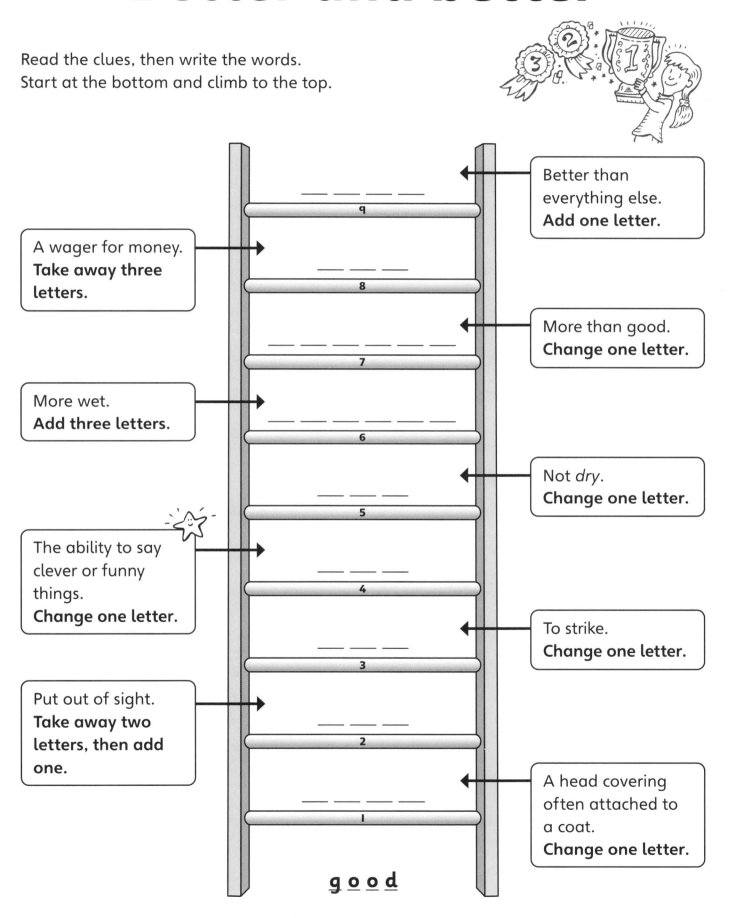

Better than everything else. Add one letter. → 9 _ _ _ _ _

A wager for money. Take away three letters. → 8 _ _ _ _

More than good. Change one letter. → 7 _ _ _ _ _ _ _

More wet. Add three letters. → 6 _ _ _ _ _ _

Not *dry*. Change one letter. → 5 _ _ _

The ability to say clever or funny things. Change one letter. → 4 _ _ _ _

To strike. Change one letter. → 3 _ _ _

Put out of sight. Take away two letters, then add one. → 2 _ _ _ _

A head covering often attached to a coat. Change one letter. → 1 _ _ _ _

g o o d

Name _____

Winter weather

Read the clues, then write the words.
Start at the bottom and climb to the top.

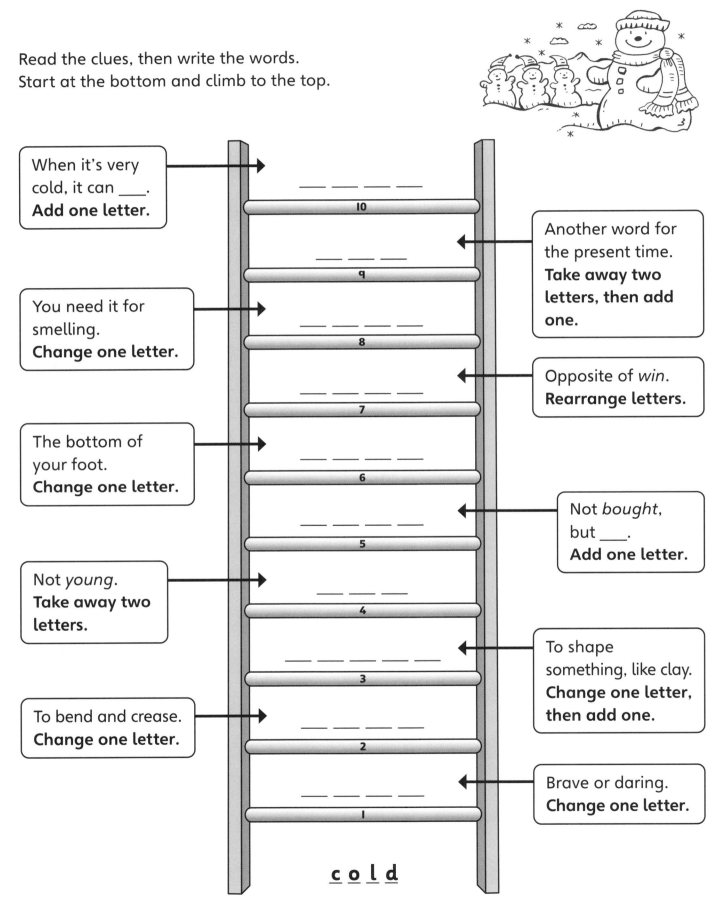

When it's very cold, it can ___.
Add one letter.
→ _ _ _ _ _
10

_ _ _
9
Another word for the present time.
Take away two letters, then add one. ←

You need it for smelling.
Change one letter.
→ _ _ _ _
8

_ _ _ _
7
Opposite of *win*.
Rearrange letters. ←

The bottom of your foot.
Change one letter.
→ _ _ _ _
6

_ _ _ _
5
Not *bought*, but ___.
Add one letter. ←

Not *young*.
Take away two letters.
→ _ _ _
4

_ _ _ _ _
3
To shape something, like clay.
Change one letter, then add one. ←

To bend and crease.
Change one letter.
→ _ _ _ _
2

_ _ _ _ _
1
Brave or daring.
Change one letter. ←

<u>c</u> <u>o</u> <u>l</u> <u>d</u>

Daily Word Ladders for Fluency **SCHOLASTIC**

Name _____

Brrrrr

Read the clues, then write the words.
Start at the bottom and climb to the top.

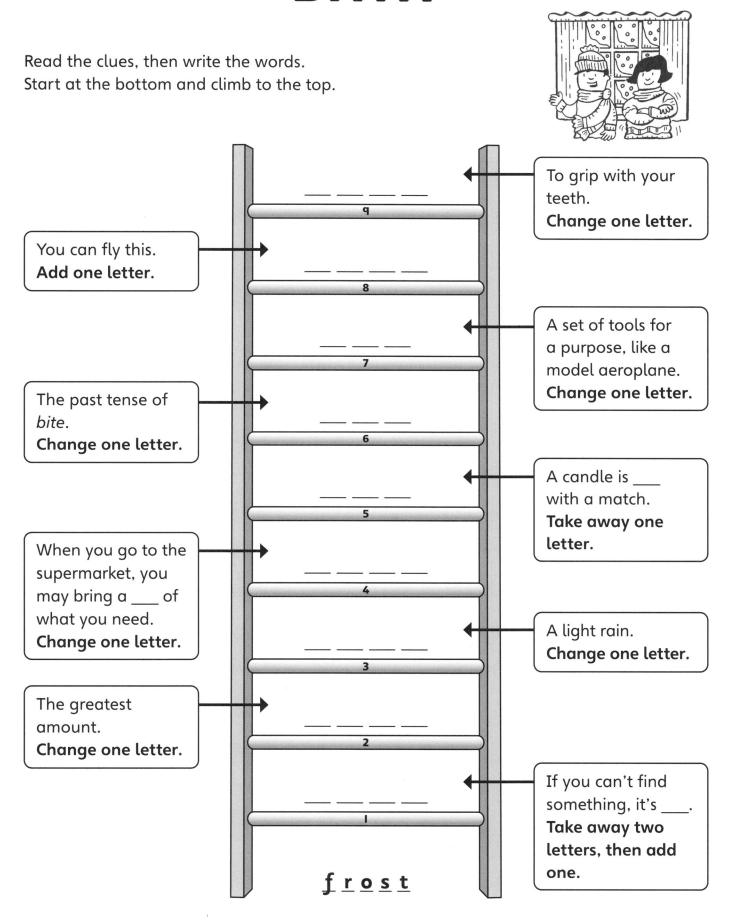

To grip with your teeth. **Change one letter.**

You can fly this. **Add one letter.**

A set of tools for a purpose, like a model aeroplane. **Change one letter.**

The past tense of *bite*. **Change one letter.**

A candle is ___ with a match. **Take away one letter.**

When you go to the supermarket, you may bring a ___ of what you need. **Change one letter.**

A light rain. **Change one letter.**

The greatest amount. **Change one letter.**

If you can't find something, it's ___. **Take away two letters, then add one.**

f r o s t

Name _____

Animal enemies

Read the clues, then write the words.
Start at the bottom and climb to the top.

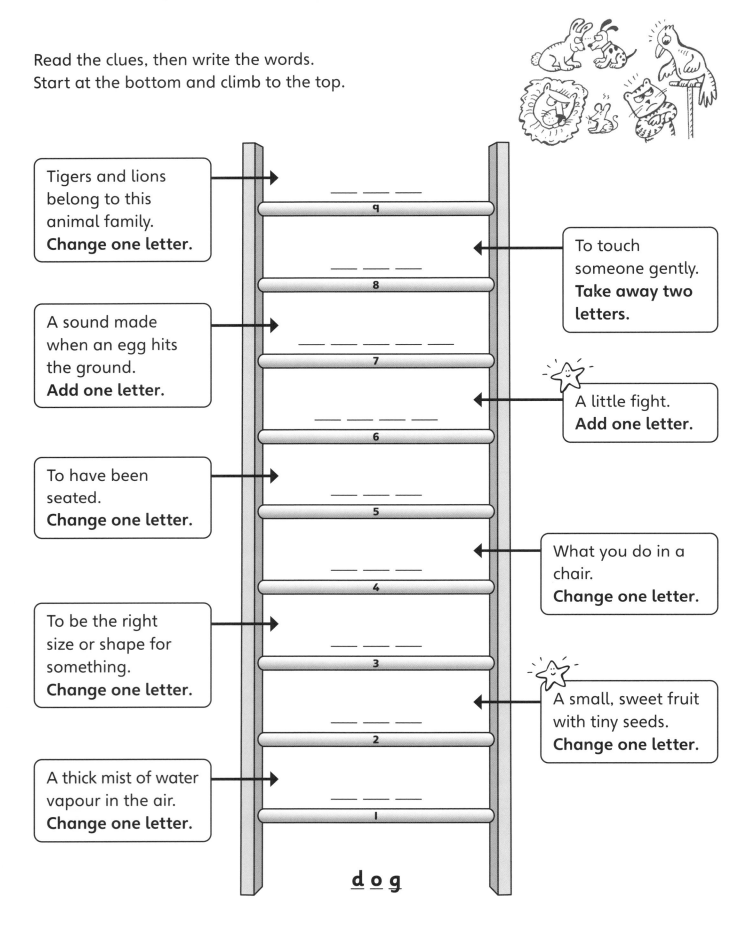

Tigers and lions belong to this animal family. **Change one letter.**

9 ___ ___ ___ ___

To touch someone gently. **Take away two letters.**

8 ___ ___ ___

A sound made when an egg hits the ground. **Add one letter.**

7 ___ ___ ___ ___ ___

A little fight. **Add one letter.**

6 ___ ___ ___ ___ ___

To have been seated. **Change one letter.**

5 ___ ___ ___ ___

What you do in a chair. **Change one letter.**

4 ___ ___ ___ ___

To be the right size or shape for something. **Change one letter.**

3 ___ ___ ___

A small, sweet fruit with tiny seeds. **Change one letter.**

2 ___ ___ ___ ___

A thick mist of water vapour in the air. **Change one letter.**

1 ___ ___ ___

<u>d</u> <u>o</u> g

Five senses

Read the clues, then write the words.
Start at the bottom and climb to the top.

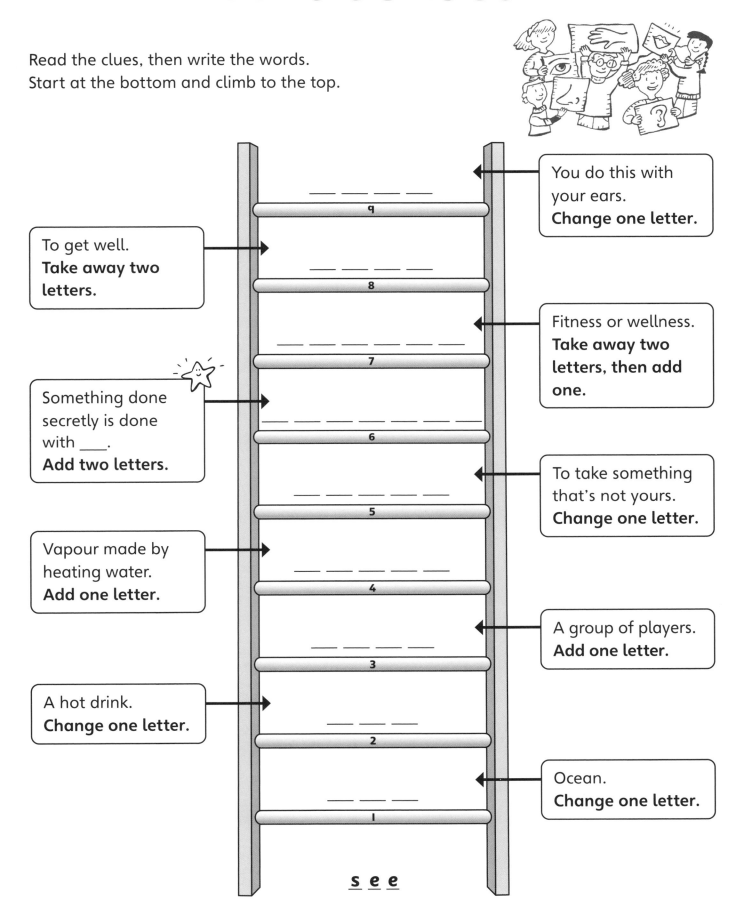

You do this with your ears. **Change one letter.**

To get well. **Take away two letters.**

Fitness or wellness. **Take away two letters, then add one.**

Something done secretly is done with ___. **Add two letters.**

To take something that's not yours. **Change one letter.**

Vapour made by heating water. **Add one letter.**

A group of players. **Add one letter.**

A hot drink. **Change one letter.**

Ocean. **Change one letter.**

9
8
7
6
5
4
3
2
1

s e e

Name _____

Shop until you drop

Read the clues, then write the words.
Start at the bottom and climb to the top.

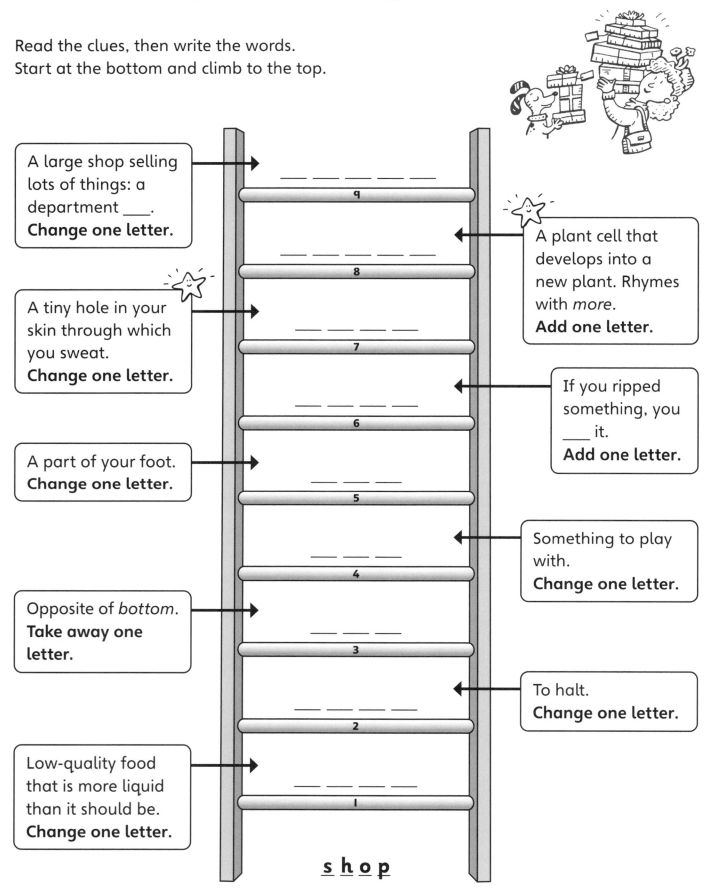

A large shop selling lots of things: a department ___.
Change one letter.
(rung 9)

A plant cell that develops into a new plant. Rhymes with *more*.
Add one letter.
(rung 8)

A tiny hole in your skin through which you sweat.
Change one letter.
(rung 7)

If you ripped something, you ___ it.
Add one letter.
(rung 6)

A part of your foot.
Change one letter.
(rung 5)

Something to play with.
Change one letter.
(rung 4)

Opposite of *bottom*.
Take away one letter.
(rung 3)

To halt.
Change one letter.
(rung 2)

Low-quality food that is more liquid than it should be.
Change one letter.
(rung 1)

<u>s</u> <u>h</u> <u>o</u> <u>p</u>

Daily Word Ladders for Fluency **SCHOLASTIC**

Name _____

Cross-country

Read the clues, then write the words.
Start at the bottom and climb to the top.

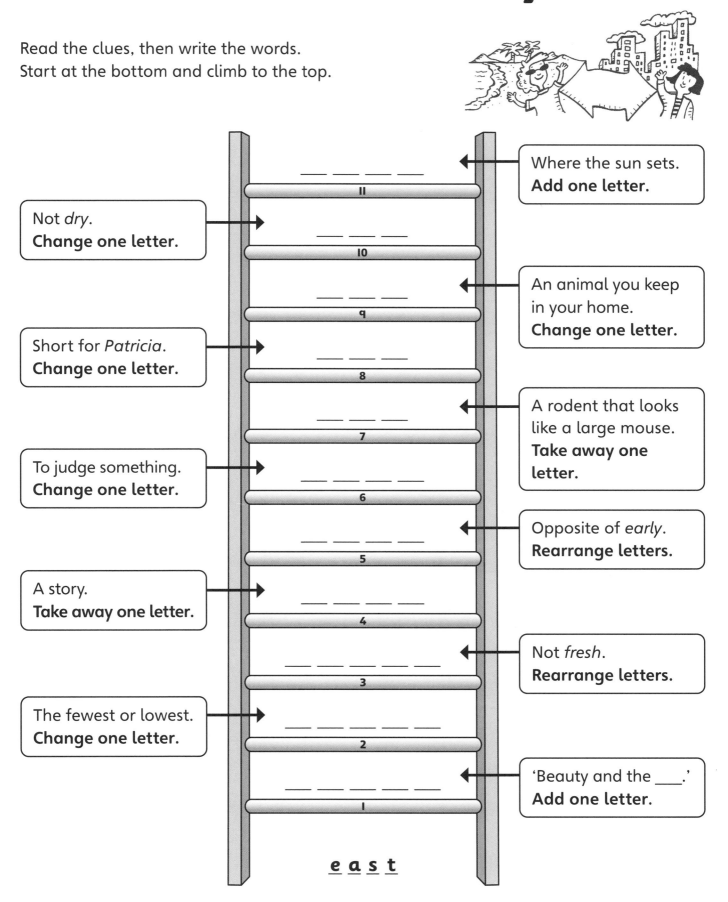

Where the sun sets.
Add one letter.

Not *dry*.
Change one letter.

An animal you keep in your home.
Change one letter.

Short for *Patricia*.
Change one letter.

A rodent that looks like a large mouse.
Take away one letter.

To judge something.
Change one letter.

Opposite of *early*.
Rearrange letters.

A story.
Take away one letter.

Not *fresh*.
Rearrange letters.

The fewest or lowest.
Change one letter.

'Beauty and the ___.'
Add one letter.

e a s t

Name _____

The whole story

Read the clues, then write the words.
Start at the bottom and climb to the top.

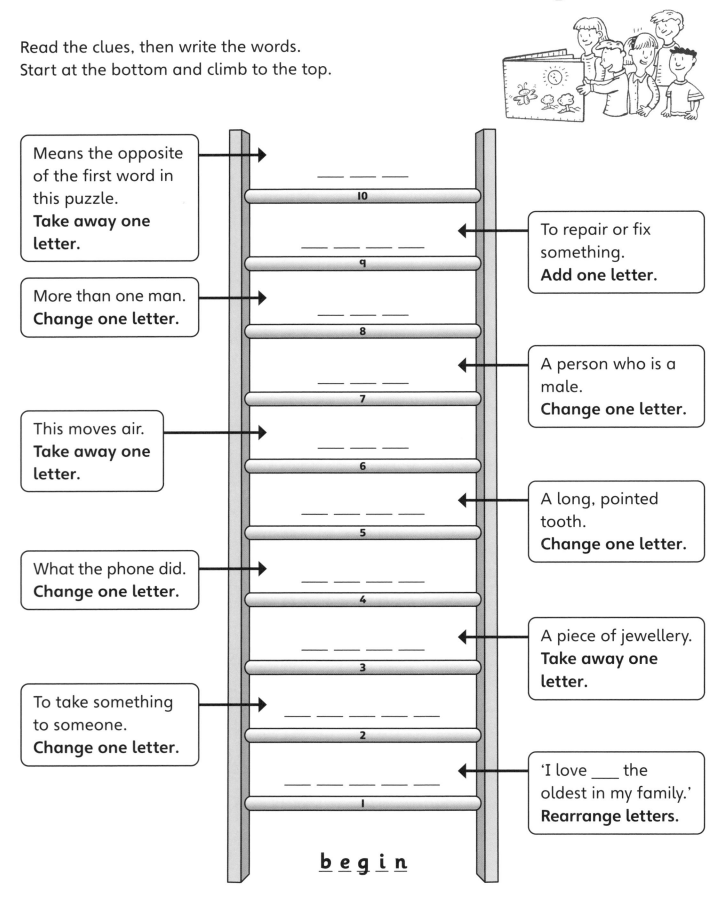

Means the opposite of the first word in this puzzle.
Take away one letter.

— — — (10)

To repair or fix something.
Add one letter.

— — — — — (9)

More than one man.
Change one letter.

— — — (8)

A person who is a male.
Change one letter.

— — — (7)

This moves air.
Take away one letter.

— — — (6)

A long, pointed tooth.
Change one letter.

— — — — (5)

What the phone did.
Change one letter.

— — — — (4)

A piece of jewellery.
Take away one letter.

— — — — (3)

To take something to someone.
Change one letter.

— — — — — (2)

'I love ___ the oldest in my family.'
Rearrange letters.

— — — — — (1)

b e g i n

Daily Word Ladders for Fluency ■SCHOLASTIC

Name _____

Rags to riches

Read the clues, then write the words.
Start at the bottom and climb to the top.

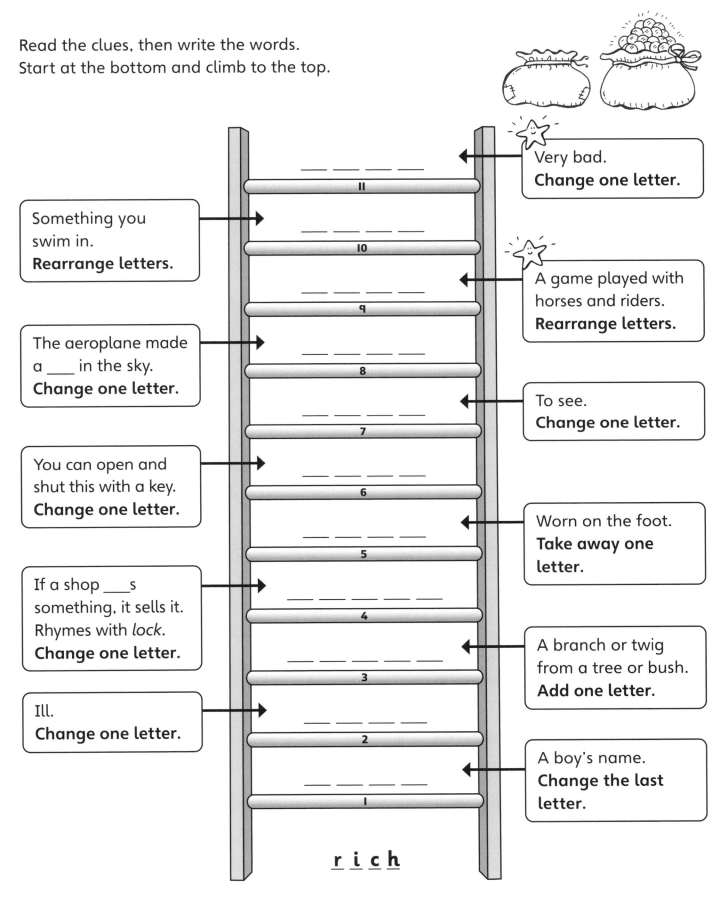

Very bad.
Change one letter.

Something you swim in.
Rearrange letters.

A game played with horses and riders.
Rearrange letters.

The aeroplane made a ___ in the sky.
Change one letter.

To see.
Change one letter.

You can open and shut this with a key.
Change one letter.

Worn on the foot.
Take away one letter.

If a shop ___s something, it sells it. Rhymes with *lock*.
Change one letter.

A branch or twig from a tree or bush.
Add one letter.

Ill.
Change one letter.

A boy's name.
Change the last letter.

r i c h

Name _____

Insect incline

Read the clues, then write the words.
Start at the bottom and climb to the top.

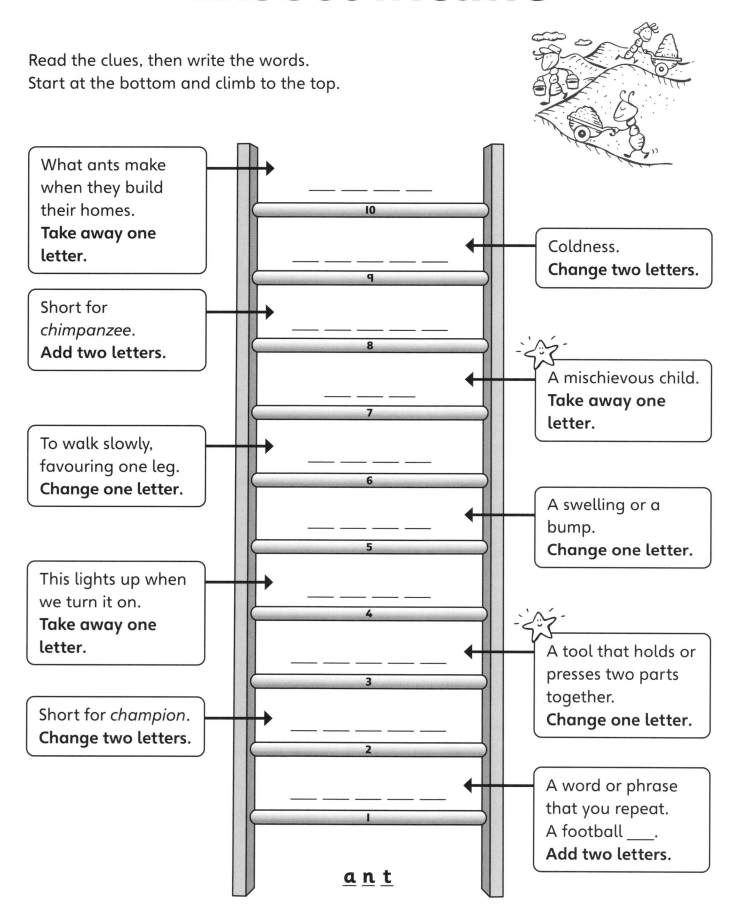

What ants make when they build their homes. **Take away one letter.**
→ 10 _ _ _ _

Coldness. **Change two letters.**
← 9 _ _ _ _ _ _

Short for *chimpanzee*. **Add two letters.**
→ 8 _ _ _ _ _

A mischievous child. **Take away one letter.**
← 7 _ _ _ _

To walk slowly, favouring one leg. **Change one letter.**
→ 6 _ _ _ _ _

A swelling or a bump. **Change one letter.**
← 5 _ _ _ _ _

This lights up when we turn it on. **Take away one letter.**
→ 4 _ _ _ _ _

A tool that holds or presses two parts together. **Change one letter.**
← 3 _ _ _ _ _ _

Short for *champion*. **Change two letters.**
→ 2 _ _ _ _ _

A word or phrase that you repeat. A football ___. **Add two letters.**
← 1 _ _ _ _

a n t

Daily Word Ladders for Fluency **■SCHOLASTIC**

Baby animals

Name _____

Read the clues, then write the words.
Start at the bottom and climb to the top.

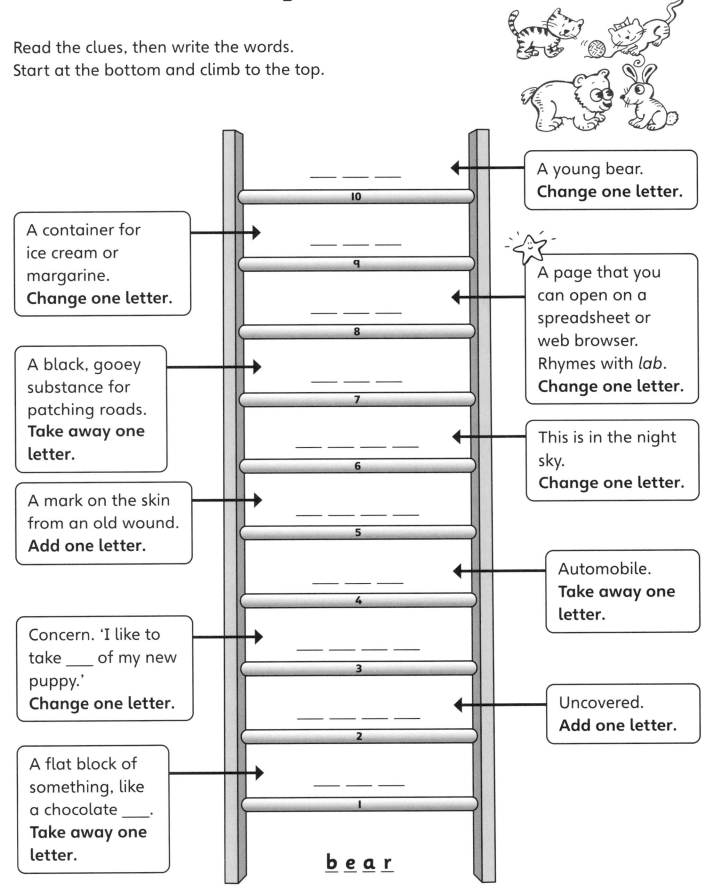

A young bear.
Change one letter.

A container for ice cream or margarine.
Change one letter.

A page that you can open on a spreadsheet or web browser. Rhymes with *lab*.
Change one letter.

A black, gooey substance for patching roads.
Take away one letter.

This is in the night sky.
Change one letter.

A mark on the skin from an old wound.
Add one letter.

Automobile.
Take away one letter.

Concern. 'I like to take ___ of my new puppy.'
Change one letter.

Uncovered.
Add one letter.

A flat block of something, like a chocolate ___.
Take away one letter.

10
9
8
7
6
5
4
3
2
1

b e a r

Name _____

Tidying up

Read the clues, then write the words.
Start at the bottom and climb to the top.

Not *dirty*.
Add one letter.

10 _ _ _ _ _

A family group.
Add one letter.

9 _ _ _ _

'You ___ do this!'
Change one letter.

8 _ _ _

A vessel used for cooking and frying food.
Take away one letter.

7 _ _ _ _

Hurt.
Take away one letter.

6 _ _ _ _ _

A liquid that you use to colour things.
Add one letter.

5 _ _ _ _ _

To breathe heavily.
Change one letter.

4 _ _ _ _

A piece of something.
Change one letter.

3 _ _ _ _

A small pointed object that you throw in a game.
Change one letter.

2 _ _ _ _

Soil.
Take away one letter.

1 _ _ _ _

<u>d i r t y</u>

Photocopiable

Daily Word Ladders for Fluency **SCHOLASTIC**

Name _____

Outerwear

Read the clues, then write the words.
Start at the bottom and climb to the top.

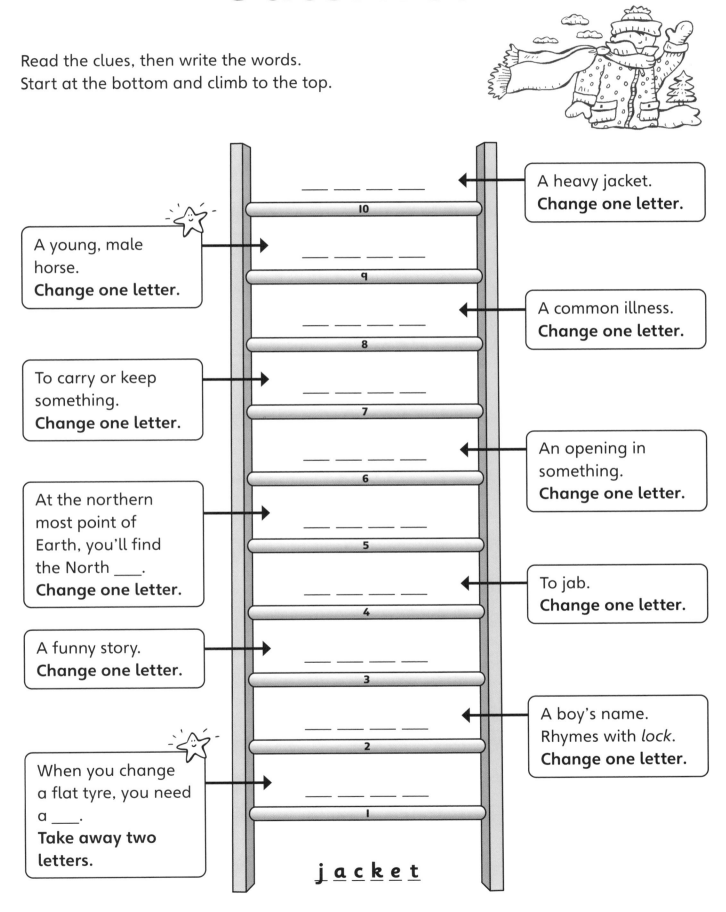

A heavy jacket.
Change one letter.

A young, male horse.
Change one letter.

A common illness.
Change one letter.

To carry or keep something.
Change one letter.

An opening in something.
Change one letter.

At the northern most point of Earth, you'll find the North ___.
Change one letter.

To jab.
Change one letter.

A funny story.
Change one letter.

A boy's name. Rhymes with *lock*.
Change one letter.

When you change a flat tyre, you need a ___.
Take away two letters.

10
9
8
7
6
5
4
3
2
1

j a c k e t

Name _____

Brass band

Read the clues, then write the words.
Start at the bottom and climb to the top.

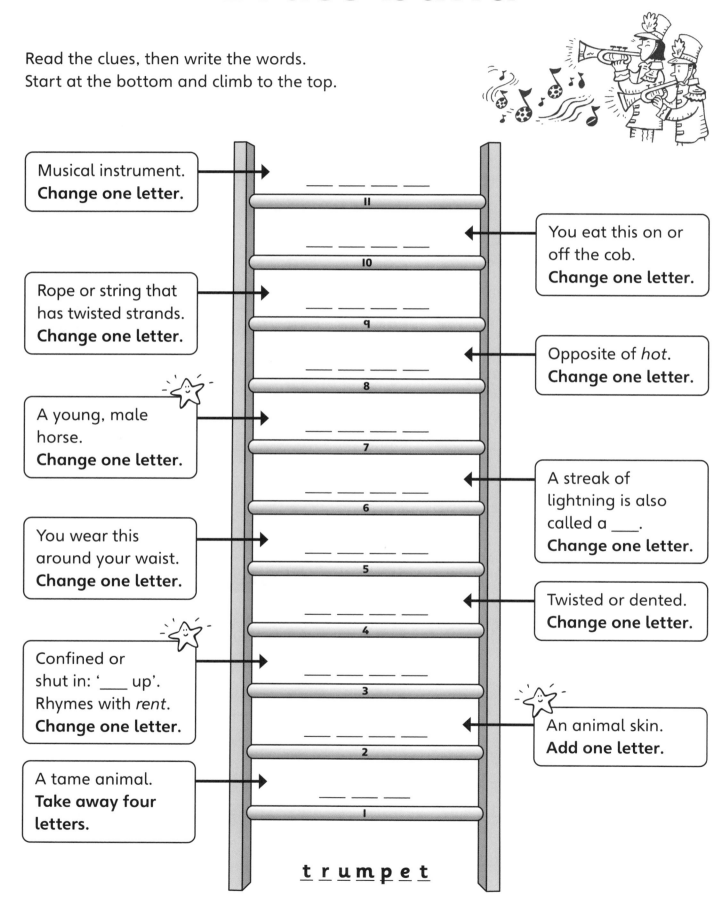

Musical instrument.
Change one letter.

You eat this on or off the cob.
Change one letter.

Rope or string that has twisted strands.
Change one letter.

Opposite of *hot*.
Change one letter.

A young, male horse.
Change one letter.

A streak of lightning is also called a ___.
Change one letter.

You wear this around your waist.
Change one letter.

Twisted or dented.
Change one letter.

Confined or shut in: '___ up'. Rhymes with *rent*.
Change one letter.

An animal skin.
Add one letter.

A tame animal.
Take away four letters.

t r u m p e t

Daily Word Ladders for Fluency **SCHOLASTIC**

Cry baby

Read the clues, then write the words.
Start at the bottom and climb to the top.

11 — — — — —

The noise made by a baby.
Change one letter.

To attempt.
Take away one letter.

10 — — — —

A flat object with raised edges, used to carry things.
Change one letter.

9 — — — — —

A device for catching things.
Take away one letter.

8 — — — —

To walk with a heavy step. Rhymes with *lamp*.
Change one letter.

7 — — — — —

A painful contraction of muscles.
Add one letter.

6 — — — — —

To stuff too many things into one place.
Add one letter.

5 — — — —

A male sheep.
Change one letter.

4 — — — —

Meat from pigs.
Change one letter.

Cut and dried grass for animals.
Change one letter.

3 — — — —

2 — — — —

Water almost completely surrounded by land.
Take away one letter.

1 — — — —

b a b y

Name _____

Utensils

Read the clues, then write the words.
Start at the bottom and climb to the top.

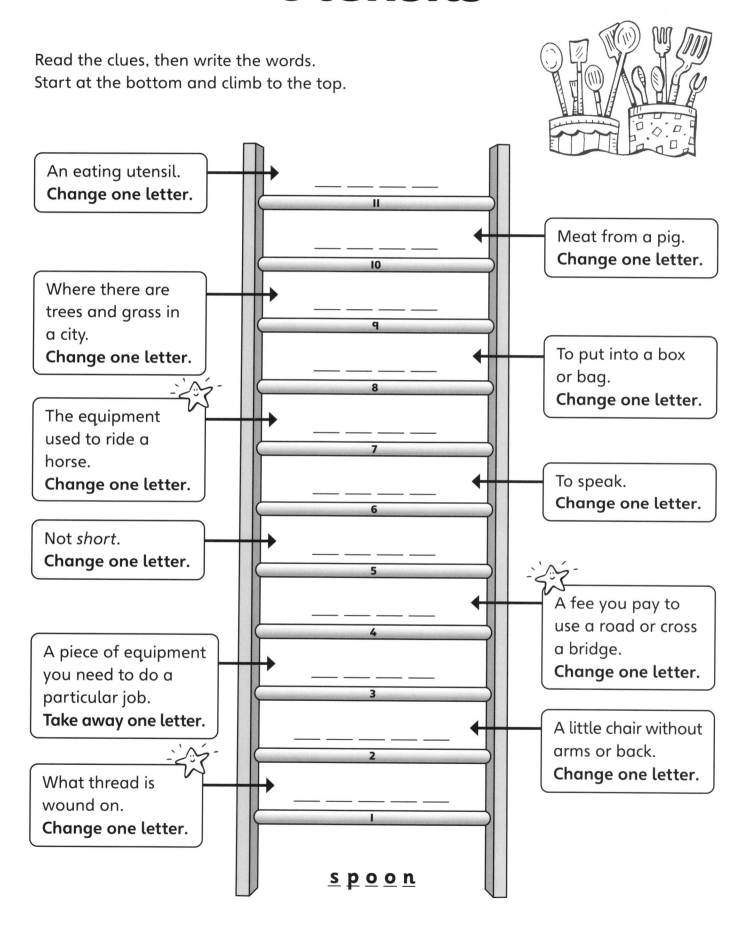

An eating utensil.
Change one letter.

Meat from a pig.
Change one letter.

Where there are trees and grass in a city.
Change one letter.

To put into a box or bag.
Change one letter.

The equipment used to ride a horse.
Change one letter.

To speak.
Change one letter.

Not *short*.
Change one letter.

A fee you pay to use a road or cross a bridge.
Change one letter.

A piece of equipment you need to do a particular job.
Take away one letter.

A little chair without arms or back.
Change one letter.

What thread is wound on.
Change one letter.

s p o o n

11
10
9
8
7
6
5
4
3
2
1

Photocopiable

Daily Word Ladders for Fluency **SCHOLASTIC**

Name _____

Wildlife

Read the clues, then write the words.
Start at the bottom and climb to the top.

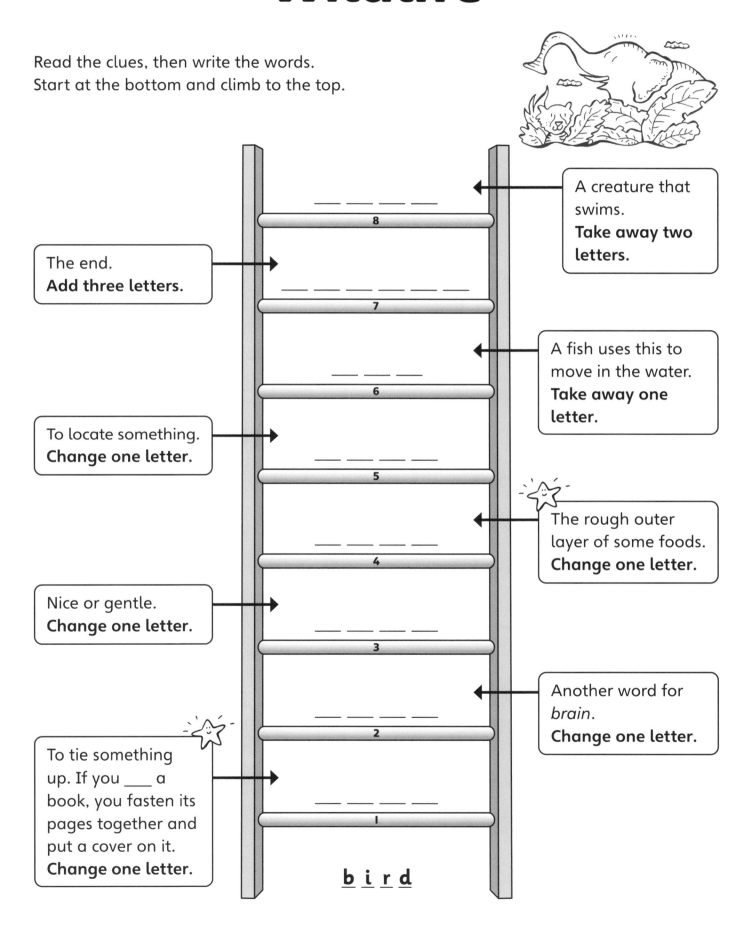

A creature that swims. **Take away two letters.**

The end. **Add three letters.**

A fish uses this to move in the water. **Take away one letter.**

To locate something. **Change one letter.**

The rough outer layer of some foods. **Change one letter.**

Nice or gentle. **Change one letter.**

Another word for *brain*. **Change one letter.**

To tie something up. If you ___ a book, you fasten its pages together and put a cover on it. **Change one letter.**

8 __ __ __ __

7 __ __ __ __ __

6 __ __ __

5 __ __ __ __

4 __ __ __ __

3 __ __ __ __

2 __ __ __ __ __

1 __ __ __ __

<u>b i r d</u>

Boo!

Read the clues, then write the words.
Start at the bottom and climb to the top.

Along with *trick*, this is often said at Halloween. **Change one letter.**

9 _ _ _ _

8 _ _ _ _ _

Wonderful or marvellous. **Rearrange the last three letters.**

Something you do to cheese when you break it into lots of tiny bits. **Change one letter.**

7 _ _ _ _ _

6 _ _ _ _ _

An elegant way of moving. Also, a girl's name. **Change one letter.**

To copy a picture, you might ___ it. **Add one letter.**

5 _ _ _ _

4 _ _ _ _

A contest to reach a goal first. **Change one letter.**

A framework for holding or hanging things, like a coat ___. **Take away one letter.**

3 _ _ _ _ _

2 _ _ _ _ _

To break or split. **Change one letter.**

What trains ride on. **Change one letter.**

1 _ _ _ _

t r i c k

90 Photocopiable

Daily Word Ladders for Fluency ■SCHOLASTIC

Name _____

Bedridden

Read the clues, then write the words.
Start at the bottom and climb to the top.

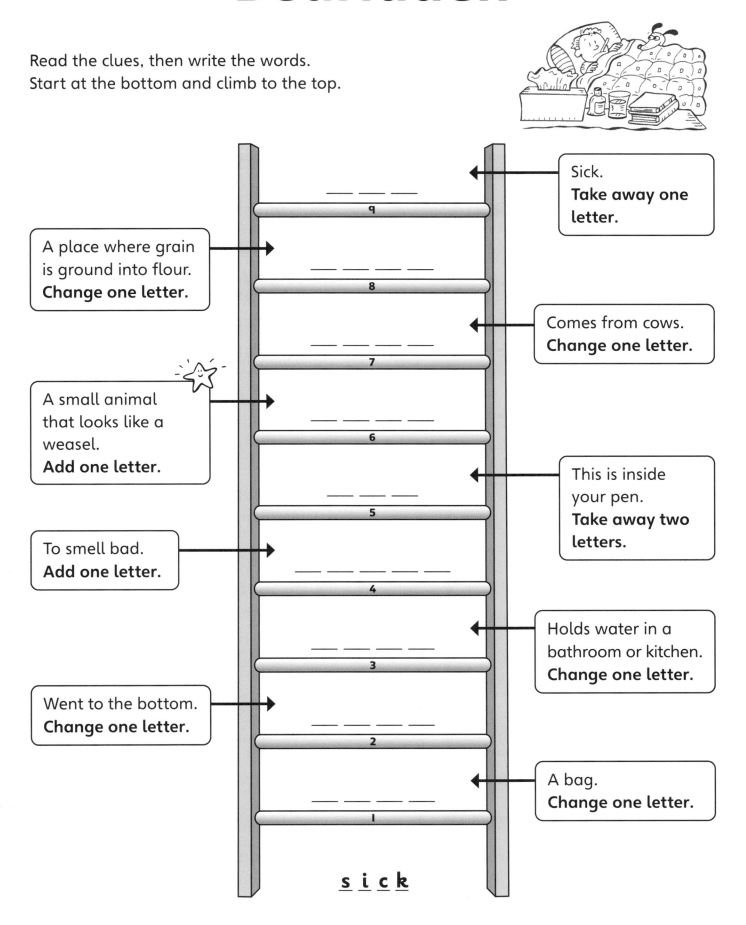

Sick.
Take away one letter.

A place where grain is ground into flour. **Change one letter.**

Comes from cows. **Change one letter.**

A small animal that looks like a weasel. **Add one letter.**

This is inside your pen. **Take away two letters.**

To smell bad. **Add one letter.**

Holds water in a bathroom or kitchen. **Change one letter.**

Went to the bottom. **Change one letter.**

A bag. **Change one letter.**

9

8

7

6

5

4

3

2

1

s i c k

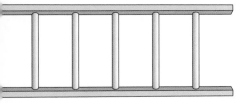
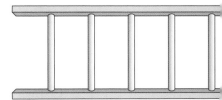

Answers

The first word for each page is the bottom of the ladder, the last word is the top of the ladder.

Counting up (page 8)
few, new, now, mow, meow, men, hen, ten, tan, man, many

Home, sweet home (page 9)
wigwam, wig, wag, sag, Sam, same, some, home

Shrinking sizes (page 10)
little, lit, it, ill, mill, mall, small

All wet (page 11)
wet, we, well, bell, belt, bet, bat, bad, Brad, bran, ran, rain

Go, go, go (page 12)
team, meat, tame, take, tale, tall, toll, Tom, torn, worn, work

Sweet seasons (page 13)
spring, string, sting, sing, sling, slim, slime, slimmer, simmer, summer

Art smart (page 14)
art, cart, car, cat, vat, sat, saw, raw, straw, draw

Bedtime (page 15)
sleep, seep, sheep, peep, peel, pail, pal, lap, clap, slap, sap, nap

More or less (page 16)
most, mast, mask, cask, cast, coast, cost, lost, last, least

Hair care (page 17)
hair, chair, char, chart, charm, harm, arm, ram, rat, rut, cut

Inside out (page 18)
door, floor, flop, lop, lip, lit, wit, win, wind, window

Dogs (page 19)
dog, dot, Don, nod, cod, code, cope, cone, bone

Restful holiday (page 20)
hotel, hot, hat, hate, haste, host, shot, shoot, sheet, sleep

Gardening (page 21)
flower, flow, slow, show, shower, shopper, shop, stop, top, pot

Shady glade (page 22)
shade, shape, shame, same, Sam, sap, sip, seep, see, tee, tree

Transportation (page 23)
boat, float, moat, mat, pat, pan, plan, plank, plant, plane

Good cooking (page 24)
fried, freed, feed, fed, bed, bad, bar, bark, barn, bare, baked

Finish line (page 25)
start, tart, cart, cast, cash, wash, wish, dish, fish, finish

Fireworks (page 26)
fire, tire, tile, pile, pill, hill, hall, hand, handle, candle

Opposites attract I (page 27)
black, block, clock, lock, look, loot, lot, hot, hit, white

Seasoning selection (page 28)
salt, sat, hat, hot, shot, shop, hop, pop, popper, pepper

Displays of affection (page 29)
hug, hog, hoe, shoe, show, slow, low, lot, lit, kit, kite, kiss

Neigh-bours (page 30)
horse, hoe, hop, hope, cope, cone, bone, bond, pond, pony

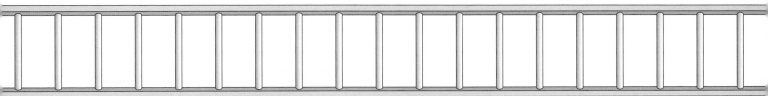

Giving and receiving (page 31)

present, sent, gent, bent, belt, bet, bit, lit, lift, gift

Getting there (page 32)

walk, talk, stalk, stall, tall, tell, ten, tent, rent, runt, run

Splish splash (page 33)

swim, swam, swan, wand, wind, win, wind, wild, wood, wool, pool

Fancy footwear (page 34)

shoe, shop, shot, shock, sock, dock, dot, hot, hoot, boot

Woodcutter (page 35)

chop, shop, slop, loop, coop, hoop, hood, food, wood

Wonderful whales (page 36)

whale, while, whole, hole, home, some, sole, sold, sod, pod

Friendship (page 37)

friend, end, trend, tend, send, sand, band, bad, pad, pal

Great grapes (page 38)

grape, grope, rope, rose, raise, raisin

Busy bees (page 39)

bee, bet, bat, bit, hit, fit, fin, fine, file, fire, five, hive

Personality change (page 40)

nice, mice, mine, mint, pint, point, into, net, ten, men, mean

Ride 'em (page 41)

horse, worse, worm, warm, war, par, park, perk, port, pony

Love life (page 42)

love, dove, dome, home, hole, mole, mule, mile, Mike, like

Underfoot (page 43)

rug, bug, bag, rag, rat, tar, star, scar, car, carp, carpet

Bare feet (page 44)

shoe, show, shot, hot, hat, at, ant, and, sand, sandal

Colour change (page 45)

blue, clue, club, cub, rub, rug, rig, rip, rim, rid, red

Deep freeze (page 46)

ice, nice, twice, lice, slice, slick, lick, luck, suck, sub, cub, cube

In the kitchen (page 47)

pots, spot, pot, pet, pets, step, stop, top, tap, apt, Pat, pans

Being grateful (page 48)

thanks, think, thin, then, hen, Ben, bent, lent, lint, live, living, giving

Ship ahoy (page 49)

ship, shop, stop, step, steep, sleep, sheep, sheet, sleet, fleet

Vehicles (page 50)

truck, tuck, tack, stack, stuck, stick, stir, star, tar, tart, cart, car

Hungry (page 51)

lunch, bunch, bunk, bank, ban, bun, bin, din, dinner

Opposites attract 2 (page 52)

black, lack, lick, chick, chin, win, wine, fine, fin, fit, hit, white

Nap time (page 53)

nap, pan, pantry, try, tree, tee, tea, sea, see, seep, sleep

City living (page 54)

city, pity, pie, tie, toe, Tom, tot, tow, town

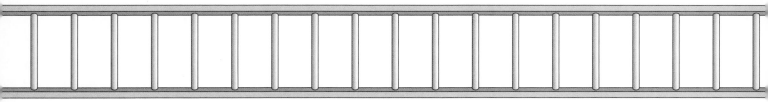

Air travel (page 55)
air, pair, pain, Spain, span, pan, pant, plant, plan, plane

Snack food (page 56)
chocolate, late, plate, plane, plan, plant, chant, champ, chimp, chip

A matter of size (page 57)
large, late, lame, lime, slime, smile, mile, male, mall, small

Catnip (page 58)
cat, sat, spat, sat, rat, hat, hot, home, hose, house, mouse

Showers and flowers (page 59)
April, lip, slip, sip, ship, shop, hop, mop, map, May

Coffee break (page 60)
coffee, fee, feet, sheet, sleet, sleep, sheep, steep, tee, tea

Simon says (page 61)
stand, sand, sad, said, paid, maid, mad, bad, bid, bit, sit

Wet and wetter (page 62)
damp, ramp, cramp, tramp, trap, part, wart, want, went, wet

After dinner (page 63)
dessert, desert, resort, sort, sore, rose, Rome, rope, ripe, pie

Bookworm (page 64)
book, boom, room, rum, hum, him, rim, rid, red, read

Daily journey (page 65)
home, come, some, Rome, more, sore, core, cord, cool, school

Top to bottom (page 66)
arm, ram, ham, hat, cat, scam, scab, cab, lab, lag, leg

Finders keepers (page 67)
find, fine, fire, fore, or, more, Rome, some, sore, rose, lose

Tolling time (page 68)
bell, ball, bull, full, fall, fill, fig, rig, ring

Some like it sweet (page 69)
sweet, tweet, wee, we, wet, set, pet, put, out, our, sour

Cricket (page 70)
ball, bell, belt, bet, get, gem, hem, ham, Sam, same, game

Good, clean fun (page 71)
clean, lean, bean, beat, bet, bat, cat, cart, dart, dirt, dirty

Gently down the stream (page 72)
row, throw, crow, crowd, cow, cod, cot, coat, float, boat

Better and better (page 73)
good, hood, hid, hit, wit, wet, wetter, better, bet, best

Winter weather (page 74)
cold, bold, fold, mould, old, sold, sole, lose, nose, now, snow

Brrrrr (page 75)
frost, lost, most, mist, list, lit, bit, kit, kite, bite

Animal enemies (page 76)
dog, fog, fig, fit, sit, sat, spat, splat, pat, cat

Five senses (page 77)
see, sea, tea, team, steam, steal, stealth, health, heal, hear

Shop until you drop (page 78)
shop, slop, stop, top, toy, toe, tore, pore, spore, store

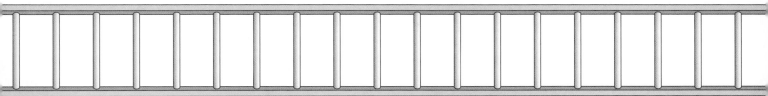

Cross-country (page 79)
east, beast, least, stale, tale, late, rate, rat, Pat, pet, wet, west

The whole story (page 80)
begin, being, bring, ring, rang, fang, fan, man, men, mend, end

Rags to riches (page 81)
rich, Rick, sick, stick, stock, sock, lock, look, loop, polo, pool, poor

Insect incline (page 82)
ant, chant, champ, clamp, lamp, lump, limp, imp, chimp, chill, hill

Baby animals (page 83)
bear, bar, bare, care, car, scar, star, tar, tab, tub, cub

Tidying up (page 84)
dirty, dirt, dart, part, pant, paint, pain, pan, can, clan, clean

Outerwear (page 85)
jacket, jack, Jock, joke, poke, pole, hole, hold, cold, colt, coat

Brass band (page 86)
trumpet, pet, pelt, pent, bent, belt, bolt, colt, cold, cord, corn, horn

Cry baby (page 87)
baby, bay, hay, ham, ram, cram, cramp, tramp, trap, tray, try, cry

Utensils (page 88)
spoon, spool, stool, tool, toll, tall, talk, tack, pack, park, pork, fork

Wildlife (page 89)
bird, bind, mind, kind, rind, find, fin, finish, fish

Boo! (page 90)
trick, track, crack, rack, race, trace, grace, grate, great, treat

Bedridden (page 91)
sick, sack, sank, sink, stink, ink, mink, milk, mill, ill